*Hyper*Graphics Corporation

TEXTNOTES TO ACCOMPANY

Computing Fundamentals
Second Edition

Peter Norton

Glencoe/ McGraw-Hill

New York, New York ■ Columbus, Ohio
Mission Hills, California ■ Peoria, Illinois

*A Division of The **McGraw-Hill** Companies*

"This Textnotes edition of *Computing Fundamentals* is published pursuant to license from the McGraw-Hill
Publishing Company."

ISBN: 002-804346-4   *Hyper*Graphics Textnotes to Accompany *Computing Fundamentals, 2nd Edition*

The *Computing Fundamentals, 2nd Edition* textbook is available from McGraw-Hill

Table of Contents

Part 1

Part 2

Software Textnotes

Part I

Preface

Instructions for the Laboratory

Computing Fundamentals, 2nd Edition

Textnotes Preface

Using Your Textnotes

The *Hyper*Graphics Textnotes for Peter Norton's *Computing Fundamentals, 2nd Edition* has been designed for use in the classroom, in the computer laboratory, and/or with the course material from the Internet. If your instructor uses *Hyper*Graphics software in the classroom, then the *Computing Fundamentals* Textnotes become a valuable note-taking tool. If you use the *Hyper*Graphics software in your computer laboratory or at home, then the Textnotes can be used as a study guide to accompany the course material encountered in an interactive computer session.

The combination of your textbook, *Hyper*Graphics software, and the *Computing Fundamentals* Textnotes provide you with a complete, interactive, and graphic learning experience. *Hyper*Graphics Textnotes include these features in every chapter:

- Multiple **key word** and **phrase** fill-in-the-blanks.
- **Graphic** support of concepts and instruction.
- **Outline activity**.
- Concept relevant **questions**.

Textnotes and Software in the Classroom

When your instructor uses *Hyper*Graphics software in the **classroom**, your Textnotes provide you with a complete note-taking assistant. Your Textnotes are organized to correspond with the textbook on a chapter-by-chapter and topic-by-topic basis.

As your instructor delivers course material using the *Hyper*Graphics software, follow along in your Textnotes and fill in key words of instruction. Textnotes are designed to support your learning process and allow you to focus on the course material without taking extensive notes.

Periodically questions appear on-screen. These questions are also listed at the end of each chapter in the Textnotes. As a question is delivered to the classroom, you can locate the question at the end of the chapter and write-in the correct answer to that question.

When you have completed a chapter in the *Computing Fundamentals* software, your Textnotes should reflect the following:

- Additional notes have been added
- Questions and blanks have been filled in

Textnotes and Software in the Laboratory or at Home

The use of Textnotes in a **laboratory** or home setting is similar to classroom use. However, the instructor is not available to direct you. So, the challenge is to move through the course material on your own and at your own pace, filling in the key points in your *Computing Fundamentals* Textnotes, answering the questions on your laboratory or home computer, and marking the correct answers to the review questions in your Textnotes.

Your textbook can serve as a reference, can be used for additional examples, and can serve as an information source for additional software questions. The Textnotes are designed to support your learning process as you move through the course material on the computer and capture, in hard copy format, the basic course material of your interactive computer session.

As you work on the computer, you can fill in the Textnotes, make notations in the margins about questions that you may still have regarding the course material, and, in general, move through the course material more thoroughly. You can also use the Textnotes as an aid so you won't just scroll through the computer material in a mechanical fashion without truly comprehending the instruction.

The following information provides the instruction you need to use *Hyper*Graphics software on your own. The use of the word "laboratory" represents individual work on school computers or computers connected to the Internet.

The Windows Desktop for Computing Fundamentals

If the *Hyper*Graphics software has been properly installed on your computer, you will have the following program group on your desktop.

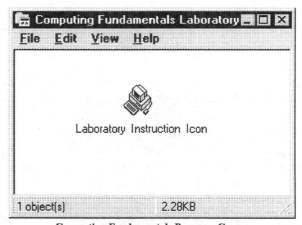

Computing Fundamentals Program Group

The **Laboratory Instruction Icon** accesses every *Computing Fundamentals* software chapter that corresponds to your *Computing Fundamentals* textbook.

Computing Fundamentals

Laboratory Instruction

Starting an Interactive Laboratory Session

To initiate the laboratory session:

1. Double-click the **Laboratory Instruction** icon.
2. When you activate the software, you must supply your user name; that is, a name, set of initials or other identification, in the **Student Logon** dialog box, pictured below.
3. Click **OK**.

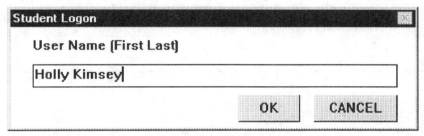

Student Logon Dialog Box

⌐ **NOTE**:   Be consistent in the entry of your name since your performance results will be identified by the name that is entered at this point. For example, if your name is Holly Kimsey, you should consistently enter that name. Do not enter the name Holly Kimsey one time and the name HJ Kimsey another time, since your results will be compiled in two different files.

3. An additional dialog box appears asking for the file name in which to save the performance results. Initially it is given a default performance file name, **student.dbf**. The default **Performance Filename** dialog box for the IPC working directory is pictured below.

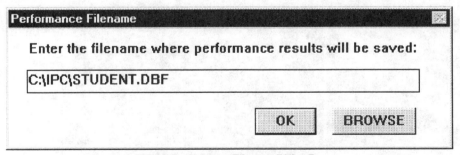

Default Performance Filename Dialog Box

If your instructor does not provide you with a specific file name to enter at this point, you should click **OK** and continue the laboratory session in the default setting. Your performance results will accumulate in the file **student.dbf**. This file provides you with concrete data that supports the progress you make in the instructional material.

4. Click **OK**.
5. Click anywhere on-screen to progress through a series of introduction screens and arrive at a **Chapter Menu**.

6. Click the chapter you want to begin.
7. Next, a **Component Menu** lists 7 distinct instructional avenues for the chapter you selected.

Each component offers a unique teaching tool that you can use to review course material. Click any component title to view its first instruction page. Each component is explained below.

Media Index	This component contains the transparencies and video teaching tools for the chapter.
Objectives	An outline of learning goals. This is an excellent way to measure progress throughout the duration of the class.
Instructional Topics	Chapter concepts and review materials are presented primarily in this component.
Action Summary	This component represents a complete overview of chapter material.
Interactive Review	Provides a post-test environment with selected questions from the Instructional Topics component.
Instructional Index	A menu of all the key terms associated with a chapter. Click on a key term to review its definition.

Instructional Topics Component

Since the **Instructional Topics** component offers the most concentrated textbook teaching material, this preface describes it in detail. Select the **Instructional Topics** component to activate the **Chapter Concepts** menu.

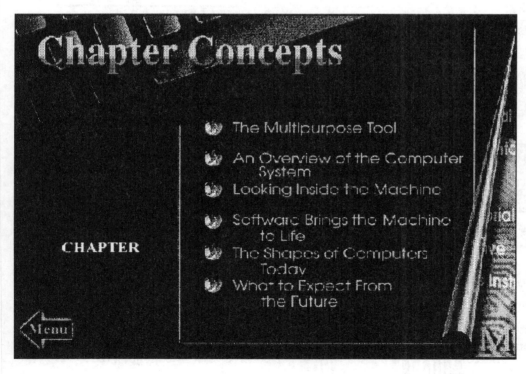

To start a fully interactive laboratory session, select a concept. The Chapter Concepts list for Chapter 1 is illustrated.

You should now be at the first instructional page of the concept you selected. To effortlessly move through the instruction, use the toolbar at the top of the page. The following chart describes the function of each icon on the toolbar.

	Click the **Help** icon for on-line information about the instructional page.
	The **Key** icon provides direct access to a list of the chapter's key terms. Click a term to review the definition. Click **Return** to go back to your instructional page.
	Click this directional icon to go to the beginning of the **previous** page.
	Each instructional page uses text and graphics to explain the chapter concept. **Use this icon to move through each page.**
	Click this directional icon to go the beginning of the **current** page.
	Click this directional icon to go to the beginning of the **next** page.
	Click the **MAP** icon to view an outline of the Chapter Concepts, with subpoints. Use this outline to keep your thoughts organized as you progress through the software, or use it as direction to specific areas of instruction. At the bottom of the page you can click **M** and go to the Chapter Concepts list, or click **R** and return to the most previous instruction page.

Remember, your Textnotes are coordinated with the *Computing Fundamentals* software so you can use both as necessary. When you select a chapter concept and move through it using the toolbar, the software progresses through every chapter concept on the list. Upon completing the final chapter concept, the software takes you to the Component Menu. Then from the Component Menu, you can select a different component.

Answering Questions in the Laboratory Session

When you encounter a question in the session, the software does not require that you answer that question to proceed to the next page. That is one of the many benefits to the laboratory environment; you can review the entire chapter of course material before you answer any questions if you want. If you read a question that you do not want to answer right away, simply use the **Next** page icon in the instructional toolbar to proceed.

When you read a question that you want to answer, follow these steps:

1. Think about the question in the context of the previous instructional material.
2. **Click** anywhere outside of the toolbar to view the possible answers.
3. **Click** your response from the on-screen answer choices.

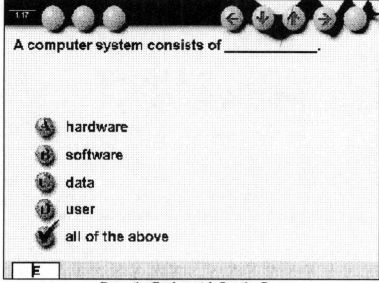

Computing Fundamentals Question Page

4. Follow any on-screen instructions.
5. Repeat steps 1-4 for each question you answer.

Online Help

For detailed instructions about the use and functions available with this software, please refer to the online help file, accessible by clicking the Help icon on the toolbar.

Now, you are ready to begin using the Textnotes in conjunction with the software. Remember, the Textnotes is a representation of the actual software and includes portions of the on-screen text to keep your attention and emphasize important concepts.

Part II

Computing Fundamentals

Textnotes for Students

CHAPTER 1
THE AMAZING COMPUTER

Directions

The Textnotes are a note taking and study aid.
- Fill in the Textnote blanks as you proceed through the software instruction.
- Any Textnote reference to computer commands such as "Click…" should be performed by you or your instructor, depending on the instructional setting.

Objectives

When you complete this chapter, you will be able to do the following:

- Discuss some of the many ways computers have an impact on our lives.
- List the four parts of a computer system.
- Recognize four kinds of computer hardware.
- Explain the purpose of software.
- List the common types of computers available today and describe what kind of job each does best.

The Multipurpose Tool

Today, the most common type of computer you'll see is called a _____ _____.

The modern PC is more powerful than its room-sized predecessors.

Early computers were used primarily to perform complex numerical tasks.

In the _____, computers began to revolutionize the business world. IBMs System/360 became the standard of its day.

The large size and cost of these machines was accepted and expected.

In the _____, Digital Equipment Corporation (DEC) introduced the PDP-11 and VAX computers. As technology increased, the size and cost of computers significantly decreased.

Computers in Business

Computers affect almost every aspect of business from _____ to _____, and more. Car manufacturers use them to build cars. Shipping companies use them to track packages all over the globe.

Medicine and Health Care

In medicine today, computers are used for everything from _____ _____ to controlling the movement of _____ _____ assistants.

A pacemaker is an example of a small, special purpose computer that has helped increase the life expectancy rate.

Education

Unlike a recorded television show, CAE, _____ _____ _____, programs can engage students through interactivity and multimedia.

Interactive tutorials can:
- Teach
- Test for understanding
- Reteach based on how much the student has learned

Science

Scientists use computers to _____ theories, _____ and test data, and exchange _____ electronically with colleagues around the world. Scientists also use computers to test theories, analyze data, and exchange data electronically with robots on other planets.

Engineering

Designing objects with a computer is called _____.

Manufacturing

Manufacturing with computers and robotics is called _____ _____. Computers can be used to perform laborious and dangerous tasks with more efficient and safer results.

In this _____ automobile assembly line, robot arms lift parts into position and weld them in place.

Legal Practice

Computer services, such as _____ and _____ allow attorneys to search quickly through huge collections of information, called _____. Courtrooms today have computers that court reporters use to translate shorthand into readable text.

Law Enforcement

Police officers use _____ _____ to access databases containing vehicle registrations and information on suspected felons. Display terminals are connected by radio to central computers. This allows law enforcement officers to access information more quickly.

Government

The federal government uses computers in many different ways. For example, computers are used to:

- automatically assign social security numbers.
- process census data.
- calculate and process income taxes.

The Military

Military computers keep track of what may be the largest _____ and _____ _____ systems in the world. Computers have also proven to be one of the most effective weapons on the battlefield. Some of their uses are:

- Laser and satellite guidance systems
- Battlefield simulations
- Storing intelligence information
- Controlling navigational instruments for ships and planes

Music

The _____ _____ _____ _____ _____ allows electronic instruments and computers to be connected. Computers allow users to do everything from writing notes to printing out the sheet music.

Theater, Film, and Television

Astounding computerized _____ _____ have been achieved in the motion-picture industry. In the first fully computer-animated movie "Toy Story," 160 _____ were used to render this monumental movie. Each frame used 300 megabytes of memory. The total for the movie was 1 terabyte or about 1,099,000,000,000 bytes.

Computers at Home

You are probably familiar with some of the advancements that computers have brought to the home. The majority of "home computers" are actually _____, or _____, inside household appliances.

An Overview Of The Computer System

The term _____ refers to the part of the computer you can touch. When most people talk about a computer, they mean _____.

The term _____ refers to sets of _____ instructions that tell the hardware what to do. Examples include:

- Personal software
- Business software
- Entertainment

_____ refers to the raw facts the computer can manipulate. Data consists of:

- Letters
- Numbers
- Sounds
- Images
- Any raw facts the computer can manipulate

In discussions about computers, people are usually referred to as _____.

This is a laptop user.

Bytes :- unite enough storge to hold one character from the keyboard

Looking Inside The Machine

Each piece of a computer system falls into one of four categories:

The Processor

The complex procedure that transforms raw data into useful information is called _Processing_
To perform this transformation, the computer uses two components: the CPU and memory.

1. The CPU is plugged into a _Circuit Board_
2. The processor (CPU) _organizes_ and carries out instructions from the user or the software.

CPU → Central Processing unit

Memory

The most common type of memory is called _RAM_ (or random access memory).

RAM needs a constant supply of _Power_ or everything in RAM disappears. RAM is mainly used to temporarily store instructions the computer needs.

Memory is measured in units called bytes.

A kilobyte (KB) is approximately _1000 Bytes_

A megabyte (MB) is approximately _1 million_.

A gigabyte (GB) is approximately _1 billion_.

Input and Output Devices

Input devices accept _data_ and _Instruction_ from the user. The most common input device is the _Keyboard_. The keyboard accepts _Letters, numbers_, and _Commands_ from the user.

In addition to the keyboard, the _mouse_ is used to give commands. The mouse allows commands to be given by _Pointing_ and _Clicking_.

Output devices _return_ processed data and information back to the user. The most common output devices are the display screen, known as the _monitor_, and the _Printer_.

The computer sends output to the monitor when the user only needs to see the output. From the monitor, the _Output_ goes to the printer when the user needs a physical, or hard copy.

Among the many different kinds of communication devices, the most common are _modem_
Modems allow computers to _communicate_ through the telephone lines. *Communicate*

KB is exactly 1024 Bytes

Storage

The purpose of storage is to _hold_ data like a filing cabinet. The most common medium is the _magnatic DISK_

Read/write head which are similar to the heads of a tape recorder or VCR, float above and below the disk near its surface.

The device that holds the disks is called a _disk Drive_

Diskets are used to load new programs or data onto the hard disk, to trade data with other users, or to make a backup copy of the data on the hard disk. The most common type of storage after the hard and diskette drives is the _CD- Rom drive_

Compact disks, or _CDS_, are a type of optical storage device that can store about 650 MB, or about 450 times as much information as a diskette.

Software Brings The Machine To Life   _Saftware_

The ingredient that allows a computer to perform a certain task is _~~CPS~~_. A specific set of instructions that drives a computer to perform a specific task is called a _Program_.

Operating Systems   _Like DoS_

When you turn on your computer, it goes through several steps to prepare itself for use. First, the computer does a _SeLF test_ to determine the amount of memory it has and if it is functioning properly. This routine is initiated by a part of the system software located in _Rom_ _____ _____.

Next, the computer looks for the _Operating systems_ and loads it into memory.

The Operating System tells the computer how to interact with the user and how to use devices such as:

- Disk drives
- Keyboards
- Monitors

When the computer has recognized that everything is working properly, Windows will start up.

_P.O.St_
Power on SeLf test

Application Software

Application Software tells the computer how to accomplish specific tasks for the _user_ Examples include:

Word Processing Programs

Word Processing Sofware can be used to create almost any kind of document.

- Term papers
- Business letters
- Legal documents
- Newsletters
- Books

Desktop Publishing Software

N/A

A desktop publishing program _____ the output of word processors and graphics programs to design printer-ready pages.

Spreadsheets

Spreadsheet programs are number crunchers which display a large grid of _Colm_ and _Rows_ that you can view.

Database Management Software

Database software extends your ability to _organise_ collections of _Data_ stored in your computer and provides _tools_ for listing _Subsets_ of the data that meet specified criteria.

When organizing information, you can organize it by:

Name	Product number
Company	Product ID
Geographic region	Supplier
Birth date	Alphabetically and so on

Graphics, Multimedia, and Presentation Applications

Programs that manipulate images are known as _Graphics Programs_. A type of application that incorporates images, text, sound, computer animation, and video is known as _Multimeidia Saftware_

Presentations Applications help you create professional looking visuals for presentations.

Entertainment and Education Software

Computer based games have brought arcade quality games to the home.

Many entertainment programs can also be considered _Educational_ software; such as astronomy programs that re-create stars and planets in space.

Many of these programs are educational and entertaining, and have been nicknamed "edutainment". The most common examples of "edutainment" programs are:

- Tutorials
- Games
- Simulations

Educational programs have been designed for everything from Astronomy to Zoology.

Utilities

Windows 95 comes with "tools" for taking care of your disks.

One of these tools is a ScanDisk program. Using the ScanDisk program can keep your hard disk free from using damaged areas.

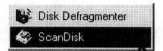

Communications Software

With a _Modem_ and a communications program, a _user_ can trade information with another _user_.

Network Sufware lets users create a network.

Services like this one allow you to hook up to services ranging from stock quotes to the _world wide wib_

The Shapes Of Computers Today

There are four different types of computers:

Supercomputers

Supercomputers are the most powerful computers made, built to process huge amounts of _____. Because computer technology changes so quickly, the advanced capabilities of a supercomputer today may become the standard features of future _____.

Next year's supercomputer will be vastly more powerful than today's.

Mainframe Computers

When a large organization needs access to the same information, _____ computers are used. A _____ is wired to the mainframe for access.

Minicomputers

The best way to explain the capabilities of a _____ is to say that they lie somewhere between those of mainframes and those of personal computers. Like mainframes, minicomputers can handle a great deal more _____ and _____ than personal computers can.

Although some minis are designed for a single user, many can handle dozens or even hundreds of terminals.

Personal Computers

When people use the terms _____, _____, and _____, they mean the small computers that are commonly found in offices, classrooms, and homes.

The terms microcomputer and personal computer are interchangeable.

_____ stands for personal computer. In 1981, IBM called its first microcomputer the IBM PC. Within a few years, many companies were copying the IBM design, creating _____ (or _____) that aimed at functioning just like the original. The vast majority of microcomputers sold today are part of this family.

One of the sources of the PC's popularity is the rate at which improvements are made in technology. _____, _____, and _____ keep getting faster and bigger.

Compared to the typical PC of ten years ago, a machine of the same price today will have:

- Eight times as much _____.
- Twenty times more storage capacity.
- Microprocessor that is at least twelve times faster.

Desktop Models

The most common type of personal computer is the _____ model.

The most common designs are the _____ and _____ models.

The only difference between the two models is that the main case, which is called the _____, of the tower model sits upright.

Tower units are often placed on the floor to preserve desk space. The tower's design has more room for adding hardware devices, such as _____, a _____, or _____.

Personal computers can cost anywhere from $1,000 to $7,500, depending on their capabilities and capacity.

This Gateway 2000 P5-133 is an example of a high-end PC that comes with a:

- Pentium processor
- 16 MB of RAM
- 2.5 gigabyte hard drive
- CD-ROM
- monitor

Notebook Computers

_____, as their name implies, approximate the shape of an 8 ½ by 11-inch notebook and can easily fit inside a briefcase.

Also called _____, they can operate with standard current or with special batteries.

Personal Digital Assistants

_____ _____ _____ are the smallest of portable computers. Often they are no larger than a checkbook. PDAs are much less powerful than notebook or desktop models. PDAs, also called _____, are usually used for special applications, such as:

- Creating spreadsheets
- Storing telephone numbers and addresses
- Organizing dates and agendas

Some PDAs, like this Apple Newton Message Pad ®, come with an _____ that lets users write on a touch-sensitive screen.

The latest generation of PDAs can use infrared light to communicate with nearby computers.

Workstations

At the other end of the spectrum, in terms of PC power, are the machines sometimes called
_____. Workstations are usually used by individuals who need a great deal of number-crunching power.

What To Expect In The Future

In the future, computers will offer more power for less money. In addition, computer manufacturers will pack more power into smaller packages.

Perhaps the most important change that will take place in the computer industry is a continued explosion in connectivity. The computers you use, whether at home, at school, or at work, are going to be connected to the computers other people use.

CHAPTER OUTLINE ACTIVITY

INSTRUCTIONS: The Chapter Outline Activity lists the instructional concepts and topics of this chapter in the order in which they appear. Fill in the outline's blanks with the correct word or phrase to better understand the chapter concepts. The number of blanks represent the number of words per response, while the length of the blanks do not represent the word length.

The Multipurpose Tool
Computers in Business
Medicine and Health Care
Education
Science
Engineering
Manufacturing
Legal Practice
Law Enforcement
Government
The Military
Music
Theater, Film, and TV
Computers in Home

An Overview Of The Computer

Looking Inside The Machine

_____ _____

_____

Input ____ _____ _____

_____

Software Brings The Machine To Life

_____ _____

_____ _____

_____ _____ Programs

_____ Publishing Software
Spreadsheets
Database Management Software

Graphics, _____ and
    Presentations Application
Entertainment and Education
Utilities
Communications Software

The Shapes Of Computers Today

_____

_____ _____

_____

_____ _____

Desktop Models

_____ Computers
Personal Digital Assistants

_____

What To Expect In The Future

REVIEW QUESTIONS

1. The first computers were used for complex numerical tasks.

   True
   False

2. Since the 1970s, computers have continually grown in physical size while providing more power for less money.

   True
   False

3. Computers are currently being used in which of the following businesses?

   a. banks
   b. grocery stores
   c. car manufacturers
   d. all of the above

4. Small, special-purpose computers have been developed which actually operate within the human body to help the body function better.

   True
   False

5. CAE, in reference to interactive learning tools, stands for _____.

   a. Carefully Audited Education
   b. Chiefly Additive Education
   c. Computer-Aided Education
   d. Computer Assurance Education

6. Without computers, space exploration would be impossible.

   True
   False

7. CAD systems are an abbreviation for _____.

   a. Challenge-Assisted-Design
   b. Computer-Aided Design
   c. Computer Analysis Directory
   d. Centrally-Affected

8. Manufacturing with computers and robotics is called CAM, or _____.

   a. Computer-Animated Movement
   b. Computer-Assisted Machinery
   c. Computer-Aided Manufacturing
   d. Computer-Activated Movement

9. Attorneys are now able to search quickly through huge collections of data, known as _____.

   a. Databases
   b. Compu-Files
   c. Infobases
   d. Case-files

10. Display terminals connected by radio to central computers are known as _____.

    a. Mobile units
    b. Mobile data terminals
    c. Centralized communications
    d. Terminal-to-terminal systems

11. The most useful number, from a computer stand- point, that the United States government assigns each individual citizen is their _____ number.

    a. Telephone
    b. Bank account
    c. Social Security
    d. Frequent Flyer

12. The military utilizes computers aboard ships, sub- marines, and airplanes, but they really don't use them in weapons or satellites.

    True
    False

13. Musical Instrument Digital Interface (MIDI) is a system that synchronizes _____ and _____ that produce electronic tones.

    a. instruments, voices
    b. hardware, software
    c. keyboards, sound waves
    d. violin, drums

14. Computers have been useful in theater and film in which of the following ways?

    a. editing films
    b. astounding special effects
    c. realistic animation
    d. all of the above

15. Computers are only contained in household devices.

    True
    False

16. Computers have radically altered business practices in the United States of America, but their impact hasn't been felt globally.

    True
    False

17. Which item below is not a computer hardware device?

    a. printer
    b. monitor
    c. directory tree
    d. mouse

18. The term software refers to programs that tell the user what to do.

    True
    False

19. Data can consist of _____.

    a. letters
    b. numbers
    c. images
    d. sounds
    e. all of the above

20. People are usually referred to as users.

    True
    False

21. A computer system consists of _____.

   a. hardware
   b. software
   c. data
   d. user
   e. all of the above

22. The complex procedure that transforms raw input data into useful information for output is called _____.

   a. conceptualizing
   b. processing
   c. transforming
   d. computing

23. 4 megabytes of memory consists roughly of _____ bytes.

   a. 4,000
   b. 10,000
   c. 4,000,000
   d. 10,000,000

24. Which of the following is not an input device?

   a. keyboard
   b. scanner
   c. printer
   d. mouse

25. Which of the following is not an output device?

   a. printer
   b. joystick
   c. monitor
   d. stereo speakers

26. The computer's main "filing cabinet" is the _____.

   a. floppy disk
   b. hard disk
   c. magnetic tape
   d. CD-ROM

27. A computer can function with just a processor, memory and input/output devices.

    True
    False

28. During the self-test, the computer looks for devices that are attached to it.

    True
    False

29. A word processor can be used to write book reports, newsletters, and even books.

    True
    False

30. Desktop publishing software merges the concepts of word processors and graphics programs.

    True
    False

31. The areas created on a spreadsheet where the columns and rows intersect are called
    _____.

    a. spaces
    b. bytes
    c. cells
    d. suites

32. Database software extends your ability to organize the data stored in your computer.

    True
    False

33. Types of applications that incorporate images, text, sound, computer animation, and video are known as _____.

    a. word processors
    b. desktop publishers
    c. graphics programs
    d. presentation applications

34. Educational programs have been developed in which of the following areas?

    a. Astronomy
    b. Geography
    c. Anatomy
    d. All of the above

35. Utility programs only come with your PCs operating system.

    True
    False

36. Modems are no longer needed in communication software.

    True
    False

37. _____ tell(s) the computer how to accomplish specific tasks for the user.

    a. Disk drives
    b. Operating-system software
    c. Application software
    d. DOS

38. Although the hardware of a computer is capable of performing marvelous tasks, it can't accomplish any of them without the vital instructions that software provides.

    True
    False

39. The software of a computer consists of _____.

    a. memory'
    b. disk storage
    c. programs
    d. a processor

40. Today's PCs are tomorrow's supercomputers.

    True
    False

41. Mainframe computers are used where many people in a large organization need frequent access to the same information.

    True
    False

42. The best way to explain the capabilities of a minicomputer is to say that they lie somewhere between those of mainframes and those of personal computers.

    True
    False

43. IBM introduced the PC in

    a. 1980
    b. 1981
    c. 1982
    d. 1983

44. The only difference between the two desktop models is that one has a bigger hard drive.

    True
    False

45. Notebook computers need special batteries to operate if there is not a standard current available.

    True
    False

46. Personal digital assistants (PDAs), the smallest of portable computers, are also known as
    _____.

    a. notebooks
    b. desktops
    c. laptops
    d. palmtops

47. The most powerful personal computer is the _____.

    a. desktop model
    b. notebook computer
    c. Personal Digital Assistant
    d. workstation

48. The largest type of computer in common use is the _____.

    a. supercomputer
    b. mainframe
    c. minicomputer
    d. microcomputer

CHAPTER 2
PROCESSING DATA

Directions

The Textnotes are a note taking and study aid.
- Fill in the Textnote blanks as you proceed through the software instruction.
- Any Textnote reference to computer commands such as "Click…" should be performed by you or your instructor, depending on the instructional setting.

Objectives

When you complete this chapter, you will be able to do the following:

- Discuss the difference between data and information.
- Explain why computers use the binary number system.
- Describe the two main parts of the CPU and explain how they work together to process data.
- Differentiate between RAM and ROM.
- Describe the hardware features that affect processing speed.
- Compare members of the best-known families of CPUs.

Transforming Data Into Information

Computers understand data through _transistors._

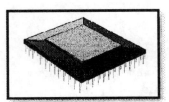

Transistors are found in the _CPU_.

Transistors capture the data that is put into the system. Data consists of the _low numbers_ that computers organize to produce information.

How Computers Represent Data

To computers everything is a number. Consider this sentence: **Here are some words.**

H	= 0100 1000	s	= 0111 0011
e	= 0110 0101	o	= 0110 1111
r	= 0111 0010	m	= 0110 1101
e	= 0110 0101	e	= 0110 0101
			= 0010 0000
a	= 0110 0001	w	= 0111 0111
r	= 0111 0010	o	= 0110 1111
e	= 0110 0101	r	= 0111 0010
		d	= 0110 0100
		s	= 0111 0011

It may look like a string of alphabetic characters to you, but to a computer it looks like a string of ones and zeros.

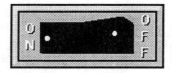

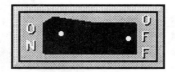

A switch has only two possible states - on and off (1 and 0).

Computers use a base 2 system, which is also known as the _Binry systems_

Bits and Bytes

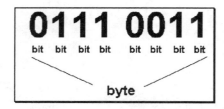

Each 0 or 1 is called a _bit_. Computers send data in groups of eight, so 8 bits is termed a _byte_.

The byte is sufficient to represent all the characters on the keyboard, including all the letters (upper and lowercase), numbers, punctuation marks, and other symbols.

Text Codes

Programmers realized that they needed a standard code for all to use. Here are the most popular:

EBCDIC

EBCDIC is an eight-bit code that defines _256_ symbols. EBCDIC is still used in IBM mainframe and mid-range systems but is rarely encountered in personal computers.

ASCII

Half# ASCII stands for the _American Standred CoDe_ for Information Interchange.

- Characters from 0 to 31 are control characters
- From 32 to 64, special characters and numbers
- From 65 to 90, uppercase letters
- From 97 to 127, lowercase letters, including a handful of common symbols

Unicode

The Unicode provides two bytes or 16 bits to each symbol for more than _65536_ different characters and symbols. This would cover every language in the world.

How A Computer Processes Data

Two components handle processing in a computer:

- The central processing unit, or CPU
- The memory

The CPU

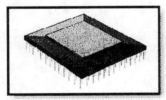

The CPU is where data is manipulated; it is commonly called the _____ of the computer.

The CPU contains two parts:

- The control unit
- The arithmetic and logic unit

The Control Unit

The control unit _____ the flow of data. The control unit _____ the instructions for the CPU. The instruction set tells the CPU how to _____ more complex operations.

New CPUs are being developed constantly. In order to save consumers money, a new CPU will include the old commands plus any new commands that may have been developed. To do this manufacturers group commands into families. This design strategy is known as _____ _____.

The Arithmetic Logic Unit

When the control unit encounters an instruction that involves arithmetic or logic, it passes that instruction to the second component of the CPU, the ALU. The ALU includes a group of _____-(high-speed memory locations built directly into the CPU) that are used to hold the data currently being processed.

The computer can only perform two kinds of operations:

- arithmetic operations
- logical operations

Arithmetic operations include:

- addition
- subtraction
- multiplication
- division
- raise by a power

Logical operations include _____:

- equal to, not equal to
- greater than, not greater than
- less than, not less than
- greater than or equal to, not greater than or equal to
- less than or equal to, not less than or equal to

Memory

There are two types of built-in memory, permanent and non-permanent.

ROM

Permanent, or _____, memory retains the data even after the computer is shut off. The data in these chips can only be read and used-it can't be changed-so the memory is called read-only memory (ROM). ROM contains a set of _____ instructions that:

- check to see that the rest of memory is functioning properly
- check for hardware devices
- check for an operating system on the computer's disk drives

Read
Only
Memory

RAM

RAM is the non-permanent, _____ memory that holds programs and data while they are in use. Every piece of data has an _____, much like a post office box number, in which it can be found very quickly. RAM stands for:

Random
Access
Memory

Factors Affecting Processing Speed

How Registers Affect Speed

The _____ of the registers, which is sometimes called the word size, indicates the amount of data with which the computer can work at any given time. Registers in the first PCs held 16 bits whereas today's registers hold _____ bits and are smaller in physical size. The 32-bit processor is twice as fast as the 16-bit.

Memory and Computing Power

The more _____ a computer has, the faster that it will likely run a program because it can load more of that program into its memory while running.

In the instance where the memory is not large enough to contain the entire program, the processor will frequently _____ _____ essential and nonessential data.

In the situation where the program fits completely in RAM, the processor will run _____ because the memory can hold the entire program, so there is no swapping.

The Computer's Internal Clock

A computer's internal clock, or _____ clock, is used to time its processing operations. The clock is driven by a piece of quartz crystal, and when electricity is applied it will vibrate millions of times per second, at a rate that never changes. The faster the vibrations the faster the processing speed will be.

The Bus

The term bus refers to the _____ between the components of a computer. There are two main buses in a computer:

- The Data Bus
- The Address Bus

The Data Bus

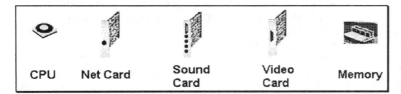

The data bus is an
_____ _____ that
connects the CPU, memory, and
the other hardware devices on
the motherboard.

Because each wire transfers one bit of information at a time, the more wires you have the faster the
processing speed will be.

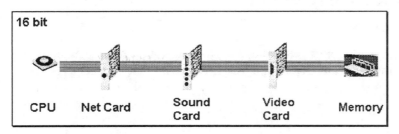

The industry standard is 16 bit
wide.

The Address Bus

The address bus carries the memory addresses of each byte of RAM. One 8-bit data represents 256
different values of memory addresses, which isn't very many. Most computers today have 32-bit
address buses that can address 4 GB (over 4 billion bytes) of RAM.

Cache Memory

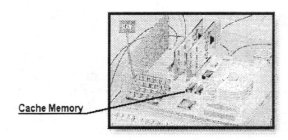

Cache Memory

Cache memory is similar to _____, except that it
is extremely fast compared to normal memory, and
it is used in a different way. Cache memory usually
holds all or part of a program's instructions.

When a program is running and the CPU needs to
read data or instructions from RAM, the CPU
checks the _____ first.

Passing Math Operations to the Math Coprocessor

The math coprocessor is a processing specialist designed to execute difficult arithmetic routines
using a _____ _____. This is a technique that translates
numbers into _____ _____.

CPUs Used In Personal Computers

The Intel Processors

Intel is not only the largest producer of chips but also the inventor of the "computer on a chip."

The 486
The first computer to have the following on a single chip:

- 386 processor
- a math coprocessor
- a cache memory controller

The Pentium
The Pentium chip is approximately five times faster than a 486 DX at the same clock speed. The Pentium's speed comes from a _____ architecture, which allows the chip to process more than one instruction in a single clock cycle.

Pentium Pro
Characteristics:

- Processes three instructions in a single clock cycle.
- Uses "dynamic execution" which refers to the chip's ability to execute program instructions in the most efficient manner, not necessarily in the order in which they were written.

The Motorola Processors

Motorola is the other major manufacturer of microprocessors for PCs.

Motorola offers two families of processor chips. The _____ family and the _____ family.

The 680x0 Series
The 68000 chip is best known as the foundation of the original Macintosh.

The PowerPC Series
_____ and Apple combined to create a chip that would dethrone Intel's dominance on the chip market. The result is the _____.

RISC Processors

Reduced instruction set computing (RISC) processors employ a theory that holds that if the instruction set for the CPU is kept _____ and _____ each instruction will execute faster.

Parallel Processing

Computers with more than one processor are known to have parallel processing capabilities. Computers with hundreds of processors are known as _____ _____ _____.

What To Expect In The Future

- Continuation in adding more cache built into the motherboard, faster clock speeds, and more instructions executed in each clock cycle.
- The increase of _____ technology.
- Adding more chips to the CPU which is known as _____.

CHAPTER OUTLINE ACTIVITY

INSTRUCTIONS: The Chapter Outline Activity lists the instructional concepts and topics of this chapter in the order in which they appear. Fill in the outline's blanks with the correct word or phrase to better understand the chapter concepts. The number of blanks represent the number of words per response, while the length of the blanks do not represent the word length.

Transforming Data Into Information

How Computers Represent _____
Bits and Bytes
Text Codes

_____

_____

_____

How A Computer Processes Data

_____ _____
    The Control Unit

    The _____ Logic Unit
Memory

    _____

    _____

Factors Affecting Processing Speed

How _____ Affect Speed

_____ and Computing Power
The Computer's Internal Clock

The Bus

_____ _____ ____

_____ _____ ____
Cache Memory
Passing Math Operations to the Math
    Coprocessor

CPUs Used In Personal Computers
The Intel Processors

_____ _____

_____ _____

_____ _____ ____
The Motorola Processors

_____ _____ _____

_____ _____ _____
RISC Processors
Parallel Processing

What To Expect In The Future

REVIEW QUESTIONS

1. Data is captured and translated by the _____ .

    a. user
    b. network
    c. keyboard
    d. CPU

2. The computer sees the alphabet as a series of ones and zeros.

    True
    False

3. There are eight characters in a byte.

    True
    False

4. This four-bit EBCDIC code is still found in mid-range systems but is rarely found in personal computers.

    True
    False

5. The ASCII text code provides:

    a. 8 characters
    b. 16 characters
    c. 32 characters
    d. 127 characters
    e. 256 characters

6. The Unicode provides 16 bytes to each symbol.

    True
    False

7. The Control Unit stores the instructions for the CPU.

    True
    False

8. The registers used by the ALU hold the instructions that are needed to process the mathematical or logical problem.

    True
    False

9. The CPU is the same as the Control Unit.

    True
    False

10. ROM can be written to.

    True
    False

11. RAM is nonvolatile memory.

    True
    False

12. Word size is the same as the _____.

    a. CPU size
    b. register size
    c. ROM
    d. speed of the register

13. A program that is larger than the computer's RAM will make the computer run slower because
_____.

    a. RAM is random access instead of sequential
    b. RAM is naturally slow
    c. RAM has to look in two different places
    d. RAM has to swap out needed information

14. The clock is driven by a(n) _____.

    a. chip
    b. transistor
    c. electrical path
    d. crystal

15. The data bus connects only hardware devices.

    True
    False

16. Every eight bits of data has a(n) _____.

    a. address number
    b. phone number
    c. serial number
    d. bus number

17. Cache memory is the same as ROM.

    True
    False

18. The math coprocessor uses a floating point unit.

    True
    False

19. The 486 was the first processor to _____.

    a. have transistors
    b. have a coprocessor
    c. be on a motherboard
    d. stand alone

20. The Pentium's speed comes from _____ architecture.

    a. a superior
    b. the dynamic
    c. a superscaler
    d. the 8-bit

21. Dynamic execution refers to the chip's ability to execute program instructions in the order in which they were written.

    True
    False

22. Motorola's 680×0 chip is best known for _____.

    a. the first microprocessor
    b. the father of microchips
    c. the original PC
    d. the original Mac

23. What two companies came together to create the PowerPC?

    a. Intel and Apple
    b. Intel and IBM
    c. IBM and Apple
    d. none of the above

24. Which company below is the maker of RISC processors?

    a. IBM
    b. Intel
    c. Apple
    d. NEC

CHAPTER 3
INTERACTING WITH THE COMPUTER

Directions

The Textnotes are a note taking and study aid.
- Fill in the Textnote blanks as you proceed through the software instruction.
- Any Textnote reference to computer commands such as "Click…" should be performed by you or your instructor, depending on the instructional setting.

Objectives

When you complete this chapter, you will be able to do the following:

- Describe the most common input and output devices.
- Understand how a video monitor displays images.
- Discuss the advantages and disadvantages of different types of printers.
- Explain how input and output devices communicate with the other parts of the computer.

The Keyboard

The keyboard was one of the first peripherals to be used with PCs and is still the most common input device.

The Standard Keyboard Layout

Keyboards for personal computers come in a number of styles that vary in _____, _____, and _____, but, except for a few special-purpose keys, most are laid out almost identically.

The most common keyboard layout used today is the IBM Enhanced Keyboard which has 101 keys arranged in four groups:

1. Alphanumeric keys
These keys are arranged in virtually the same way on every keyboard and typewriter. This arrangement is called the QWERTY layout because the first six keys on the top row of letters are Q, W, E, R, T, and Y.

Also included with the alphanumeric keys are _____ keys (such as Shift or Ctrl) that are used in conjunction with other keys.

2. Numeric keypad

The numeric keypad looks similar to an adding machine and is usually located on the right side of the keyboard.

3. Function keys

These often serve as shortcut keys to various functions of an application. What each function key does depends on the program you are using.

4. Cursor-movement keys

Located between the alphanumeric keys and the numeric keypad, they allow quick movement of the cursor without the use of the _____. Whenever working with any program that requires text to be entered, a mark appears on the screen where the text will be entered. This mark is called the cursor, insertion point, or I-beam cursor.

5. Modifier keys

These are used in conjunction with the other keys. Another key is pressed while a modifier key is held down. The modifier keys on a PC are:

- Shift
- Control (Ctrl)
- Alternate (Alt)

How the Computer Accepts Input from the Keyboard

When you press a letter or number on the keyboard, you might think the keyboard simply sends that letter to the computer ... after all, that is what appears to happen. Actually, it is more complex than that.

First, when a key is pressed, a computer chip called the _____ _____ notes the event. The keyboard controller then places the key's _____ _____, which identifies the key pressed, into a part of its memory called the _____ _____.

Next, a signal called an _____ _____, is sent from the keyboard controller to the computer's system software indicating something has occurred.

Lastly, the CPU reads the scan code from the keyboard buffer and converts it to ASCII and sends it to RAM.

The Mouse

Next to the keyboard, the _____ is the most common input device used with personal computers.

A mouse is an input device that rolls around on a flat surface (like a desk) and controls the _____.

The pointer is an on-screen object, usually an arrow, that is used to _____ _____, _____ _____, _____ _____, or _____ _____ other programs, files, or data that appear on the screen.

Using the Mouse

You use a mouse to _____ to a location on the screen.

- Push the mouse forward, and the pointer goes up on the screen.
- Move the mouse to the left, and the pointer goes to the left and so forth.

To point to an object or location on the screen, you simply use the mouse to place the pointer on _____ of the object or location. Everything you do with the mouse is accomplished by combining pointing with four other techniques:

- Clicking
- Double-clicking
- Dragging
- Right-clicking

The Inner Workings of the Mouse

The mouse is really a simple device. The most common design has a _____ enclosed inside a plastic housing. As the mouse glides over a flat surface, the ball rolls in the direction of the movement.

This motion is detected by two rollers placed at a _____ angle from each other. A sensor detects how much each roller spins and sends this information to the computer. The operating system processes the information and moves the cursor around the screen accordingly.

Taking Care of the Mouse

Because a mouse _____ around on the surface of a mouse pad or desk, it has a tendency to pick up objects scattered there, such as _____ and _____. This debris builds up over time and can inhibit the performance of the mouse. The pointer seeming to get stuck on the screen and the mouse failing to glide around smoothly are symptoms of a dirty mouse.

To clean a mouse, first remove the cover plate and ball from the underside of the mouse. Wipe the mouse _____ clean with a dry cloth and set the ball aside. If there is dust or fuzz on the _____ inside the mouse, use tweezers to remove the debris and replace the ball and cover plate.

The Trackball

The trackball is a _____ _____ that works like an upside-down mouse. The mouse ball is exposed on the top of the trackball and is manipulated with the thumb.

Trackballs have the advantage over mice in that they do not require a large area to maneuver and are therefore useful when work space is _____.

The Trackpad

The trackpad is a small, stationary pointing device that senses the movement of a _____ across its surface and translates that to cursor movement.

The small size (about 1.5 to 2 inches on a side) makes the trackpad well suited for such small work environments as a _____ _____.

Pointers in the Keyboard

One other pointing device should be noted. It consists of a small _____ positioned near the middle of the keyboard, usually between the g and h keys.

The joystick is controlled with either forefinger, while two buttons located just behind the spacebar serve the same function as mouse buttons.

Because of its small size, this pointing device is incorporated into several models of laptop computers. There is as of yet no generic name for this pointing device, although several manufacturers are referring to it as an "_____ pointing device."

Other Input Devices

While the keyboard and mouse are the primary input devices used with computers, there are other methods of data entry.

Sometimes unusual work environments or special needs warrant the use of alternative input devices.

Pens

The electronic pen is an _____ _____ that utilizes a pen to either write on a special pad or computer screen, or the pen may function as a _____ _____ to select commands.

It is important to remember that the _____ or _____ is the actual input device and not the _____.

The screen detects _____, _____, or an _____ _____ that comes from the pen and then processes the signal.

Pen-based systems are not very efficient for entering large amounts of text, but are quite adept at data collection where _____ answers are required. Many companies, like UPS for example, use pen-based storage devices for storing signatures as digital images.

Touch Screens

_____ _____ allow the user to interact with the computer by simply touching the screen. Such touch sensitive devices have sensors either in or near the screen that _____ and _____ the user's touch.

Touch screens are very useful in environments where dirt or weather would quickly render a keyboard or mouse useless. They are also used in situations where a _____, _____ interface is important and are well suited for tasks such as automated teller machines or public information kiosks.

Bar Code Readers

The most widely-used input device after the keyboard and mouse is the bar code reader.

Used extensively in _____-_____ and _____ _____, these devices convert the bar code, a pattern of printed bars on products, into a product number.

This is accomplished by the emitting of a beam, usually a _____ _____, onto the bar code and then measuring the reflected light.

The special bars at each end of the image are different, so the reader can tell whether the bar code has been read right-side up or upside down so that it can be interpreted properly. After the number on the bar code has been interpreted, the number is sent to the computer and processed as though it had been typed into the keyboard.

Image Scanners and Optical Character Recognition

An image scanner converts any image into electronic form by shining light onto the image and sensing the intensity of the reflection at every point.

Color scanners use _____ to separate the components of color into the _____ _____ _____ (red, green, and blue) at each point. Once an image is scanned into a computer's memory, it can be manipulated, with the aid of graphics software, to _____ _____, _____ _____, and even _____ the image itself.

One example of graphics manipulation, called _____, involves two scanned images that are gradually merged together. On video, it appears the two images transform from one to the other.

_____ _____ _____ (_____) software translates a scanned text image into a format that can then be used and manipulated by word processing software. OCR applications are very complex because the same character of text can appear in an almost unlimited number of ways.

This picture shows just a few ways that a lowercase g can appear in print.

Both scanned images and text are stored as _____. A bitmap is a grid of dots, each dot representing one or more bits.

Graphics and OCR applications are designed to translate these arrays of dots into a useful format that can be more easily manipulated.

Scanners come in a range of sizes, from flatbed scanners that sit on a desktop to hand-held models.

Hand-held scanners can not scan whole pages at once as can flatbed scanners, but they have the advantage of being _____ _____ as well as _____ _____.

For images that are bigger than the width of the hand-held scanner, multiple passes may be required to capture the entire image.

Microphones and Voice Recognition

In recent years, sound has become a standard feature of computers. As a result, microphones have become increasingly common input devices.
Sound is most often used in multimedia presentations which can be enhanced by _____, _____, or _____ _____.

All that is needed to produce sound is an input device, like a microphone or CD player, and a sound card.

The sound card translates _____ _____ into a digitized form, as well as converting digitized sounds back into analog signals that can be sent to speakers.

The ability for computers to receive audio input from microphones has led to the demand for software to _____ and _____ speech and translate it into text.

This technology is called voice recognition, or _____ _____, software. Voice recognition allows the user to give simple commands, such as "_____ _____" or "_____ _____", orally rather than using the keyboard or mouse.

The Monitor

Although there are a variety of input devices, currently there are only three common types of output devices:

- Monitors
- Printers
- Sound Systems

Of these three, the monitor is the most important because it is the output device the user interacts with most. There are two basic types of monitors used with PCs:

- Cathode Ray Tube (CRT)
- Flat-panel Display

Both types can be either _____, _____, or _____.

A monochrome monitor displays one color against a contrasting background (often black).

Grayscale monitors use varying intensities of gray against a white background.

Color monitors display pictures with up to thousands of colors and are now by far the most common.

How a CRT Monitor Displays an Image

A cathode ray tube (CRT) is essentially a large vacuum tube. Located at the back end of the tube inside the monitor housing is an _____ _____.

This electron gun shoots a steady stream of electrons through a magnetic coil that directs the beam towards the front of the monitor.

The back side of the monitor's screen is coated with chemicals, called _____, that glow in reaction to being struck by the electron beam.

The screen's phosphor coating is organized into a grid of small dots. The smallest number of these phosphor dots the gun can focus on is called a pixel, short for picture element.

The picture on the screen appears to be steady, but that is actually not the case. The electron beam is constantly moving from left to right, top to bottom over the screen so rapidly that the picture has the illusion of being steady. With each pass over a pixel, the intensity of the beam is adjusted to change the pixel's appearance if necessary.

A color monitor works the same way as its monochrome counterpart, except that there are three electron beams instead of just one.

The three beams correspond to the three _____ _____ _____ (red, green, and blue), although the beams themselves are colorless.

Each pixel of a color monitor is made of a tiny dot of red, green, and blue phosphor - each of which reacts separately to the corresponding electron beam.

Comparing CRT Monitors

There are so many monitors on the market that it is important to understand how to evaluate a monitor's performance. A good monitor:

- is easier on the eyes.
- allows for longer periods of usage.
- prevents eyestrain and headaches.

The factors to consider in choosing a good monitor are:

- Monitor Size
- Resolution

- Refresh Rate
- Dot Pitch

Monitor Size
A good rule of thumb with monitors is that bigger is better. The larger the monitor, the larger objects on the screen appear or the more objects you can fit on the screen.

Like televisions, monitors are measured in inches diagonally from the _____, _____ _____ to the _____, _____ _____ of the screen.

Resolution
The resolution of a monitor is defined as the _____ _____ _____ on the screen and is expressed as a _____. In other words if, a resolution of 640×480 means:

- 640 pixels horizontally across the screen
- 480 pixels vertically down the screen

Monitor resolution is actually determined by the _____ _____ and not the monitor, so most monitors have a range of resolutions.

640×480 was the VGA (Video Graphics Array) standard established by IBM in the mid-1980s. With the later emergence of the SVGA (Super-VGA) standard, resolutions expanded to 800×600 and 1024×768.

Higher resolutions generally have the advantage of a _____ _____ over lower resolutions.

Refresh Rate
While size and resolution are readily apparent and standardized, the refresh rate of a monitor is neither obvious nor standard.

Refresh rate is the number of _____ _____ _____ the electron guns scan every pixel on the screen and is measured in _____ (_____), or cycles per second.

Each time a pixel is struck by the electron beam, the phosphors glow, but this glow fades quickly after the beam passes by. Therefore, if the refresh rate is not high enough, the screen may appear to flicker which can cause eyestrain.

Generally, a refresh rate of _____ ____ _____ _____ should not cause eyestrain.

Dot Pitch

Like refresh rate, dot pitch is neither readily apparent nor standard.

Dot pitch is the _____ between the individual dots that make up an individual pixel.

Remember that one pixel on a color monitor is made up of three phosphor dots, and if these are too far apart the images on the screen will not be sharp.

Though dot pitch is hard to detect, it can still cause eyestrain anyway.

Generally, a dot pitch of _____ _____ _____ _____ will not cause problems for the user.

The Video Controller

Besides the monitor itself, the most important factor in overall video output is the video controller. The video controller is a _____ _____ inside the computer that serves as an intermediary device between the _____ and the _____.

It contains _____-_____ _____, also called video RAM or VRAM, and other circuitry necessary to send data to the monitor for display on the screen.

VRAM is most often dual-port which works slightly different than regular RAM; therefore, it is sometimes referred to as DRAM.

_____ and _____ mean the same thing.

Also called a video card, this device works within the constraints of the monitor to determine:

- resolution.
- refresh rate.
- the number of colors displayed.

As resolutions and the number of available colors have increased, so has the need for greater
_____ _____ in video controllers.

Flat-Panel Monitors

CRT monitors are well-suited to desktop computers because of their size and clarity. However, they are not practical for laptops because they are too _____ and require too much _____ to operate.

There are several types of flat-panel monitors, but the most common by far is the liquid crystal display (LCD) monitor. Liquid crystal is a kind of liquid that is normally _____ but becomes _____ when charged with electricity.

LCDs fall into two main categories:

- Passive Matrix LCD
- Active Matrix LCD

Passive matrix LCDs have a transistor for each column and row of the display, thus creating a grid that defines each pixel. The color of each pixel is controlled by _____ coming from the transistors for each point on the screen. Low refresh rates inherent in passive matrix technology were improved with the advent of dual-scan LCD. Dual-scan LCD refreshes each pixel twice as often.

Active matrix LCD technology assigns a transistor for each pixel, and every pixel is controlled individually. Refresh rates of active matrix displays are very high, so the drawbacks of passive matrix LCDs do not exist. The drawbacks to the active matrix LCD are the _____ _____ and the _____.

Printers

Besides the monitor, the most important output device is the printer. Two types of printers have become industry standards:

- Ink-jet Printers
- Laser Printers

When evaluating printers, consider the following methods of comparison:

- Image Quality   Also called print resolution; measured in dots per inch (dpi)
- Speed   Measured in the number of pages of text printed per minute (ppm)
- Cost of operation   The cost of ink or toner as well as maintenance required varies between types of printers

Ink-Jet Printers

Ink-jet printers spray ink through tiny nozzles. Though the technology is not new, it has become much more _____ and _____.

No longer are special paper or long drying times necessary with newer models.

And if color images are required, color ink-jet printers offer by far the most cost-effective way to print in color.

Typically, ink-jet printers produce _____ _____ _____ pages per minute with resolutions of at least _____ _____.

Laser Printers

Laser printers produce higher quality images and are usually _____ than ink-jet printers, but are also _____ _____.

As the name implies, laser printers use a laser to create an _____ _____ at specific points on a _____ _____.

Toner, which is tiny particles of oppositely charged ink, is transferred by _____ and _____ from the drum to the paper.

Typically, laser printers produce between ____ and _____ pages of text per minute with resolutions ranging from _____ _____ _____ _____.
Laser printers print documents faster and at higher resolutions than do ink-jet printers, but are also more expensive to purchase and maintain.

Other High-Quality Printers

Several other types of more specialized printers should also be noted:

- Thermal-Wax Printers
- Dye-Sub Printers
- Fiery Printers
- IRIS Printers
- Plotters

Thermal-Wax Printers

Thermal-wax printers are used primarily for high-quality _____ _____ where production cost is a factor.

These printers use ribbons coated with colored wax that adheres to paper when passed over by a focused heat source.

Dye-Sub Printers

Dye-sub (for dye sublimation) printers use a ribbon containing panels of color that is moved over a focused heat source.

The dyes on the ribbon evaporate onto specially coated paper where they form different colors.

Specific colors are attained by varying the intensity of the heat applied.

Fiery Printers

Fiery printers are a type of laser printer that produce _____-_____ _____ of images that will later be printed on _____-_____.

This is a highly specialized type of printer most often used by small print shops and publishers.

Iris Printers

IRIS printers are a type of ink-jet printer that produce graphics that resemble off-set printed images.

This high-end printer can produce an image with a resolution of _____ _____.

Plotters

A plotter is perhaps the most specialized type of printer and is used in conjunction with _____ _____.

It is capable of producing large drawings or images with a high degree of detail, like _____ _____ or _____.

The plotter uses a robotic arm to draw with colored pens on a sheet of oversized paper as it moves through the printer.

Sound Systems

In the last few years, sound has become an integral part of personal computing. Today, when you buy a _____ _____, you get:

- A CD-ROM
- A video controller with plenty of VRAM
- Speakers
- A sound card

At the heart of the sound system is the _____ _____. A sound card is a digital circuit board that is capable of translating _____ _____ into a _____ _____ and vice versa.

Sound is sent to the sound card via a _____ or _____, converted to a digital format, and stored in memory.

To hear a stored sound, the sound card translates the digital sound into an electric current which is sent to the speakers. With proper software, digitized sound can be manipulated or edited in any way the user desires.

Connecting I/O Devices To The Computer

To connect an I/O device to a computer, you must do so by way of the _____ _____.

To accomplish this, you must connect the device to an appropriate _____ on the back of the computer.

Most computers have several different types of ports already installed.

Serial and Parallel Ports

The data bus inside a computer consists of _____ _____ that connect the PC's components. Similarly, a _____ _____ consists of eight or more wires through which data can flow simultaneously.

Most data buses can transfer _____ _____ of information at the same time; this is called _____ _____ _____.

The standard parallel interface, however, transfers eight bits (one byte) at a time over eight separate wires.

In a serial interface, data bits are transferred one at a time over a single wire. There are other wires in a serial interface which carry the bits that control the flow of data.

The computer's bus is _____; therefore, it is necessary to convert the data to _____ when communicating with serial devices.

This is accomplished inside the computer by a special chip called a UART card. Parallel data bits enter the UART card and are converted into serial data that flows through a serial cable.

The current standard for serial communications is called RS-232. Though serial ports can have either _____ or _____ pins, the RS-232 standard still applies.

Some of the most common serial devices are:

- The mouse
- The modem

As you might expect, a _____ _____ can handle a higher volume of information than a _____ _____.

The standard parallel port has _____ _____ and is most commonly used for the _____ _____.

Printer cables have a 25-pin plug for the computer end and a 36-pin plug at the printer end.

This cable is called a Centronics interface, named for the first company to manufacture successful dot-matrix printers.

Expansion Slots and Boards

PCs are designed so the user can easily adapt, or configure, the computer to personal needs or requirements.

If the computer is not already equipped with a port required by the user, an expansion card may be installed to add it. To allow for this, PCs are designed with expansion slots which are connected to the data bus.

These slots accept circuit boards which are also called:

- Cards
- Adapters
- Boards

Notebook computers accept PC cards which are much smaller than circuit boards but do the same thing.

Expansion slots on the motherboard are used for three purposes:

1. Provide access to the bus via controller cards for built-in devices such as disk drives.
2. Provide ports for external I/O devices such as a monitor or printer.
3. Provide access to the computer for special-purpose devices like an accelerator card.

An accelerator card is a self-contained device that enhances _____ _____ through access to the computer's _____ and _____.

Many devices (like _____ _____, _____ _____, or _____) require the installation of a card into an expansion slot.

SCSI

While expansion slots are versatile, they are limited to one device per port, thus limiting the number of external devices they can support.

One device that has helped to solve this limitation is the small computer system interface (SCSI, pronounced "scuzzy"). A SCSI is in effect an _____ _____ from the computer's bus to the outside of the computer.

Just like one extension cord can be linked to another creating a longer one, so can SCSI devices be joined together.

If an external device is equipped with a SCSI connection, then it can be linked with other SCSI devices.

A series of connected SCSI devices form what is called a _____-_____. Today, with the emerging standard of _____-____, as many as _____ _____ can be linked together in one daisy-chain.

What To Expect In The Future

The most significant advances in the future will probably be in the area of human-interface technologies like:

- voice recognition
- handwriting recognition

Significant advances have been made in both technologies and should improve dramatically in the future.

But perhaps the greatest strides over the next few years will be in _____ _____, especially in the use of color. Just as color monitors have almost entirely replaced monochrome, so will color printing replace black and white.

CHAPTER OUTLINE ACTIVITY

INSTRUCTIONS: The Chapter Outline Activity lists the instructional concepts and topics of this chapter in the order in which they appear. Fill in the outline's blanks with the correct word or phrase to better understand the chapter concepts. The number of blanks represent the number of words per response, while the length of the blanks do not represent the word length.

The Keyboard
The Standard Keyboard _____
How the Computer Accepts _____ from
  the Keyboard

The Mouse
Using the Mouse
The Inner Workings of a Mouse
Taking Care of the Mouse

_____

_____
Pointers in the Keyboard

Other Input Devices
Pens

_____ _____
Bar-Code Readers

Image Scanners and _____
Microphones and Voice Recognition

The Monitor
How a CRT Monitor Displays an Image
Comparing CRT Monitors

_____ _____

_____

_____ _____

_____ _____

The Video Controller
Flat-Panel Monitors

Printers

_____-_____ Printers

_____ Printers
Other High-Quality Printers

_____-_____ Printers

___-___ Printers

_____ Printers

_____ Printers

_____

Sound Systems

**Connecting I/O Devices To The
    Computer**

Serial and _____ Ports

_____ _____ and Boards
SCSI

What To Expect In The Future

REVIEW QUESTIONS

1. Which of the following is not one of the four main groups of keys on the standard keyboard?

   a. Alphanumeric keys
   b. Numeric keypad
   c. Function keys
   d. Cursor-movement keys
   e. Help keys

2. The computer chip inside the keyboard that processes each key stroke is called the _____.

   a. keyboard buffer
   b. CPU
   c. keyboard controller
   d. motherboard

3. The processor that converts the scan code into ASCII is the _____.

   a. keyboard buffer
   b. CPU
   c. keyboard controller
   d. motherboard

4. The mouse is mainly used to _____.

   a. point to objects on the screen
   b. click and drag objects
   c. quickly move the pointer around the screen
   d. all of these

5. The most common mouse design includes all of the following except:

   a. Ball
   b. Plastic housing
   c. Optical sensors
   d. Movement sensors

6. Dust and other debris that a mouse picks up over time will not inhibit its performance.

   True
   False

7. A mouse utilizes less desk space than a trackball.

   True
   False

8. Trackpads are ideal for notebook computers because of their _____.

   a. cost
   b. performance
   c. speed
   d. size

9. An integrated pointing device is a small _____ located in the middle of the keyboard.

   a. mouse
   b. trackball
   c. joystick
   d. touchpad

10. The electronic pen, rather than the pad or screen, is the actual input device.

   True
   False

11. Electronic pen devices are not very efficient for entering large amounts of text.

   True
   False

12. Touch screens are less prone to the damaging effects of dust and weather than keyboards.

   True
   False

13. Barcodes cannot be read upside-down.

   True
   False

14. The three primary additive colors include all the following except:

   a. Red
   b. Green
   c. Yellow
   d. Blue

15. Scanned text, like a scanned image, is stored as a bitmap.

    True
    False

16. Optical Character Recognition (OCR) applications are relatively simplistic programs.

    True
    False

17. Hand-held scanners have an advantage over flatbed scanners in that they are _____.

    a. very portable
    b. less expensive
    c. easier to operate
    d. all of the above
    e. A and B only

18. Sound is most often used to enhance multimedia presentations.

    True
    False

19. Many computers can already interpret simple voice commands with the aid of voice recognition software.

    True
    False

20. Which of the following is not an output device?

    a. Monitor
    b. Mouse
    c. Printer
    d. Sound system

21. The most common output device is the monitor.

    True
    False

22. The smallest number of phosphor dots the electron gun can focus on is called a_____.

    a. cathode
    b. bit
    c. pixel
    d. byte

23. The image on a screen appears to be steady, but it is actually the result of a quickly moving electron beam.

    True
    False

24. Each pixel on a color monitor is made of two smaller phosphor dots.

    True
    False

25. Where monitors are concerned, bigger is not usually better.

    True
    False

26. Monitors are measured in inches diagonally from the lower, left corner to the upper, right corner of the screen.

    True
    False

27. Resolution is determined by the _____.

    a. monitor
    b. video controller
    c. video graphics array
    d. CPU

28. Refresh rate is measured in _____ or cycles per second.

    a. Hertz (Hz)
    b. Megahertz (MHz)
    c. Watts
    d. Amps

29. Refresh rate and dot pitch both can have an adverse effect on the user's eyes.

    True
    False

30. Dot pitch is the distance between pixels.

    True
    False

31. It doesn't really matter what model of monitor you buy, because they are all about the same.

    True
    False

32. All of the following are factors to consider in choosing a good monitor except:

    a. Monitor size
    b. Resolution
    c. Manufacturer
    d. Dot pitch
    e. Refresh rate

33. The video controller is a circuit board that serves as an intermediary device between the
    _____ .

    a. computer bus and monitor
    b. graphics array and CPU
    c. CPU and monitor
    d. graphics array and monitor

34. The video card establishes all of the following except:

    a. Dot pitch
    b. Refresh rate
    c. Resolution
    d. The number of colors displayed

35. CRT monitors are well-suited to laptops.

    True
    False

36. LCD stands for _____ .

    a. Light Conveying Device
    b. Liquid Cadmium Display
    c. Liquid Computer Display
    d. Liquid Crystal Display

37. Active-matrix LCDs have a transistor for each column and row of the display.

    True
    False

38. Passive-matrix LCDs have a higher refresh rate than do active-matrix displays.

    True
    False

39. The most common output device after the monitor is the printer.

    True
    False

40. All of the following are things to consider when comparing printers except:

    a. Image quality
    b. Speed
    c. Cost of operation
    d. Manufacturer

41. _____ are by far the most cost effective way to print in color.

    a. Laser printers
    b. Ink-jet printers
    c. Dot matrix printers
    d. None of the above

42. Laser printers produce higher quality images than do ink-jet printers but are usually slower.

    True
    False

43. Laser printer are more expensive to operate than other common printer types.

    True
    False

44. _____ and _____ printers both use heat in the printing process.

    a. Thermal-wax, fiery
    b. Dye-sub, IRIS
    c. Plotters, IRIS
    d. Thermal-wax, dye-sub

45. _____ are used in combination with CAD software.

    a. Thermal-wax printers
    b. Dye-sub printers
    c. Fiery printers
    d. IRIS printers
    e. Plotters

46. Which of the following is not part of a multimedia PC?

    a. CD-ROM
    b. Scanner
    c. Video controller
    d. Sound card

47. The heart of the sound system is the _____.

    a. sound card
    b. speakers
    c. CD player
    d. sound system software

48. Most data buses can transfer 32 bits of information simultaneously.

    True
    False

49. The device that converts parallel data to serial data is called a(n) _____.

    a. data bus
    b. UART card
    c. alternator card
    d. serial/parallel processor

50. The current standard for serial ports is RS-232.

    True
    False

51. The most common serial devices are _____.

    a. the mouse and monitor
    b. monitor and printer
    c. mouse and modem
    d. monitor and modem

52. A serial interface can transfer data faster than a parallel interface.

    True
    False

53. The most common parallel device is the _____.

    a. monitor
    b. mouse
    c. modem
    d. printer

54. PCs are difficult to configure to a user's personal needs.

    True
    False

55. Expansion circuit boards are known as all of the following except:

    a. Cards
    b. Adapters
    c. Processors
    d. Boards

56. SCSI is the abbreviation for _____.

    a. Short Cable Serial Interface
    b. Small Capacity Serial Interface
    c. Small Computer Serial Interface
    d. Small Computer System Interface

57. A series of SCSI devices linked together is called a_____.

    a. token ring
    b. daisy wheel
    c. tulip ring
    d. daisy chain

CHAPTER 4
STORING INFORMATION IN A COMPUTER

Directions

The Textnotes are a note taking and study aid.
- Fill in the Textnote blanks as you proceed through the software instruction.
- Any Textnote reference to computer commands such as "Click…" should be performed by you or your instructor, depending on the instructional setting.

Objectives

When you complete this chapter, you will be able to do the following:

- List the most common types of storage devices.
- Explain how diskette and hard disk drives work.
- Understand how data is organized on a disk.
- Explain how type drives work.
- Describe various optical storage devices.
- Discuss disk drive interface standards.

_____ _____ is the physical components on which data is stored. The hardware components that write data to, and read it from, storage media are called _____

_____.

Examples include:

- Diskette - holds 1.44 megabytes of data.
- Disk Drive - holds the diskette.
- Hard Drive - part of storage capacity that is hidden inside your computer.

Types Of Storage Devices

Two main technologies are used to store data today:

- magnetic storage
- optical storage

The primary types of
_____ _____
are:
- Diskettes
- Hard disks
- Removable hard disks
- Magnetic tapes

The primary types of
_____ storage
are:
- CD-ROM
- WORM
- Magneto-optical disks

Magnetic Storage Devices

All magnetic drives are coated with a magnetically sensitive material (usually iron oxide) which reacts to a _____ _____. Like the transistor, a magnetic field can represent on (positive field) and off (negative field). Unlike a transistor, a magnetic field doesn't need continual electricity.

The read/write heads of a hard disk drive, diskette drive, or tape drive contain _____, which charge the particles of iron on the storage medium as the head passes over the disk (hard disk or diskette) or tape. The read/write heads record strings of _____ and _____ by alternating the direction of the current in the electromagnets. To read data from a magnetic surface, the process is reversed.

Diskette Drives

These drives, often called floppy drives, or floppies, have the capability to access data _____. The heads can skip from one spot to another without having to scan everything in between. The most common uses of diskettes are as follows:

- _____ files between computers that are not connected through communications hardware.
- _____ new programs onto a system.
- _____ _____ data or programs, the primary copy of which is stored on a hard disk drive.

Types of Diskettes

The early diskettes were _____, which refers to the diameter, not the _____ of the disk. These diskettes have been replaced by the _____ type.

The higher the _____ of the disk, the more closely the iron-oxide particles are packed, and the more data the disk can store. The 5.25-inch diskette holds 720 KB, while the smaller 3.5-inch diskette holds 1.44 MB of data.

How Data Is Organized on a Diskette

To use a diskette, it must be formatted. Formatting means to map the disk into _____ of readable space.

In the formatting process, the first thing that occurs is that a set of concentric _____ are created, called tracks. The tracks are typically numbered from _____ running from the outside inward.

_____ are used to further subdivide the diskette. Each of these is numbered to create a single _____ address. Most diskettes today have the capability to use both sides.

Each sector typically contains _____ bytes with both sides of the diskette capable of storing data. DOS and Windows operating systems allocate groups of sectors, called _____, to each file stored on the disk.

How the Operating System Finds Data on a Disk

A computer's operating system is able to locate data on a disk because each track and sector is labeled, and the location of all data is kept in a special _____ on the diskette. The labeling of tracks and sectors is called performing a _____ or _____ format.

A commonly used logical format performed by DOS or Windows creates these four disk areas:

- The boot record
- The file-allocation table (FAT)
- The root folder or directory
- The data area

The _____ _____ determines whether the disk has the basic components of DOS or Windows that are necessary to run the operating system successfully. If it determines that the required files are present and the disk has a valid format, it transfers control to one of the operating system programs that continues the process of starting up. This process is called _____- because the boot program makes the computer "pull itself up by its bootstraps."

The _____ _____ _____ is a log that records the location of each file and the status of each sector. The FAT solves the problem of those files already saved but that increase in size by adding to it. The FAT checks for _____ _____ and then places _____ to link together the "extra" parts of the file. This sort of approach for increasing files causes _____ since the file parts are stored in non-adjacent sectors.

_____ or directories are tools used to organize files on a disk. Folders can contain files as well as other folders creating a hierarchical structure. The top folder on any disk is known as the _____.

The part of the disk that remains free after the boot sector, FAT, and root folder have been created is called the _____ _____ because that is where the data files are actually stored.

Hard Disks

The hard disk (drive) acts just like the _____ except that the hard disk is faster and holds much more. The disk is made of _____ platters which allows the disk to spin much faster.

The rigidity of the hard disk and the high speed at which it rotates allow a lot more data to be recorded on the disk surface. Hard disks typically contain from _____ MB on up, with most current PCs containing at least 1 GB of hard disk space.

Because hard disks are actually a stack of _____, the term cylinder is used to refer to the same track across all the disk sides.

The one drawback to the hard disk is that the read/write heads must be extremely close to the surface of the disk. If anything gets on the disk, there is a chance of a _____ _____ causing the destruction of the data that the heads contact.

Removable Hard Disks

These disks and drives attempt to combine the speed and capacity of a hard disk with the _____ of a diskette.

Hot-Swappable Hard Disks

Hot-swappable hard disks are like _____ versions of normal hard disks and allow the user to swap disks while the computer is still _____ (hot).

Hard-Disk Cartridges

Hard-disk cartridges are like diskettes in that they have a disk in a plastic case that is inserted into or removed from the _____. SyQuest drives and the Jaz drives are examples of hard disk cartridges. The _____ drive is extremely fast and can store up to 1 GB of data.

The Bernoulli Drive

A Bernoulli Drive spins, causing the air pressure to bend the disk up toward the _____ head but maintains a thin layer of air between the heads and the disk. These early drives have grown from an original capacity of 5 MB to 230 MB with speeds approaching that of a _____ _____.

Tape Drives

A tape drive acts much like an _____ cassette. The primary difference is that _____ data is written to the tape instead of the signals generated by sound in an audio recorder. Tapes are used mainly for _____ copies of your hard disk, since data is stored _____-one bit after another. Although it is _____ compared to the hard disk, it costs a lot less.

Optical Storage Devices

Today, the most popular alternatives to magnetic storage systems are _____ systems. Optical storage techniques make use of pinpoint precision that is possible only with _____ _____.

CD-ROM

Compact disk, read-only memory, or CD-ROM, uses the same technology that is used to produce _____. The CD-ROM drive reads 0's and 1's off a spinning disk by focusing a _____ on the disk's surface.

Lands are the flat areas and represent _____. Pits are the depressions and represent _____.

Two disadvantages of CD-ROMs as compared to hard disks are as follows:

CD-ROMs are much _____ than the normal hard disk in retrieving data from the CD-ROM to the computer.

Also, unlike the hard disk, you cannot _____ data to the CD-ROM directly from the computer using typical read/write heads.

CD-ROMs can hold 650 MB of data compared to 1.44 MB for diskettes. They are very popular for _____ software products since many diskettes are for many programs are over forty or fifty megabytes.

Up and Coming technology - DVD (digital video disk) a two-sided CD that can hold as much as _____ GB of data.

CD Recordable, WORM Disks, and PhotoCD

CD-Recordable (_____) drives may be attached to a computer as a peripheral device and allow the user to record their own CDs. Once the information is written to the CD, it cannot be _____.

PhotoCDs are a form of recordable CDs used for storing digitized _____ _____. WORM stands for _____ _____ _____ _____.

Magneto-Optical Drives

An MO disk has the capability of an optical disk but can be _____ with the ease of a magnetic disk.

The disk is covered with magnetically sensitive metallic _____ sandwiched inside a thin layer of plastic. To _____ to the disk, a laser melts the plastic allowing a magnet to change the orientation of the metallic crystals.

It is _____ much like the CD-ROM with a laser on the track of the crystals where the laser is either absorbed or reflected.

Measuring Drive Performance

When evaluating the performance of common storage devices, you need to be aware of two common measures:

- Average access time
- Average transfer rate

Average Access Time

The average access time is the amount of time it takes to position the _____ heads over any spot on the medium. The average access time is a combination of two factors:

- the _____ at which a disk spins
- the time it takes to _____ the heads from one track to another

Typical average access times are as follows:

- diskettes: _____ milliseconds
- hard drives: ___ to ___ milliseconds

- CD-ROM and WORM drives: _____ to _____ milliseconds
- good removable hard disks and magneto-optical disks: ___ to ___ milliseconds

Data Transfer Rate

The second important statistic for measuring drive _____ is the speed at which it can transfer data. The speed is expressed as a _____, or some amount of data per unit of time.

Hard drives: _____ to _____ MB per second
CD-ROMs: _____ KBps for double-speed up to _____ KBps for six-speed
Diskettes: _____ KBps
Removable hard disk and magneto-optical disks: _____ MBps up to _____ MBps

Drive Interface Standards

All storage devices need a _____ to act as an intermediary between the drive and the CPU.

The ST-506 Standard

The first ST-506 drives used a _____-_____ _____ called modified frequency modulation (MFM). A data-encoding scheme is the method that a disk drive uses to translate bits of data into a sequence of flux reversals on the surface of a disk.

The second generation drives employed a new data-encoding scheme called _____-_____ _____ (RLL). The RLL-encoding scheme made more efficient use of the _____ space on a hard disk.

Integrated Drive Electronics

The integrated drive electronics (IDE) interface places most of the disk controller's circuitry on the _____ itself to provide a simpler interface with the computer and more reliable operation than was possible with the older ST-506 drives. This was originated by _____ _____ Corporation and Enhanced IDE currently supports rates up to _____ MBps.

Enhanced Small Device Interface

A less popular controller developed by _____ Corporation incorporated most of the circuitry of the controller directly into the drive.

Small Computer System Interface

The SCSI (pronounced _____) was developed so that third-party _____ devices could connect to computers. One way to think of SCSI is as an extension of the computer's _____. All of the controller's _____ is incorporated into the SCSI drive. The SCSI drive:

- improves efficiency.
- accommodates multiple devices.

What To Expect In The Future

- _____ hard disk drives that are faster, hold more, and are cheaper.
- _____ that will hold more data, up to 4.5 GB.
- _____ techniques that can store thousands of gigabytes (GB) in crystals the size of sugar cubes.
- Computers without storage devices that interface to the _____ (time will tell if this idea of computers without storage will catch on).

CHAPTER OUTLINE ACTIVITY

INSTRUCTIONS: The Chapter Outline Activity lists the instructional concepts and topics of this chapter in the order in which they appear. Fill in the outline's blanks with the correct word or phrase to better understand the chapter concepts. The number of blanks represent the number of words per response, while the length of the blanks do not represent the word length.

Types Of Storage Devices

Magnetic Storage Devices
Diskette Drives
Types of Diskettes

How Data Is _____ on a Diskette

How the _____ _____
   Finds Data on a Disk
Hard Disks

_____ Hard Disks

_____-_____ Hard Disks

Hard Disk _____

The _____ Drive
Tape Drives

Optical Storage Devices

_____-_____
CD-Recordable, WORM Disks, and
   PhotoCD
Magneto-Optical Drives

Measuring Drive Performance

_____ _____ Time

_____-_____ Rate

_____-_____ Standards
   The ST-506 Standard
   Integrated Drive Electronics
   Enhanced Small Device
      Interface
   Small Computer System
      Interface

What To Expect In The Future

REVIEW QUESTIONS

1. The physical devices that permanently maintain data and information are referred to as computer media.

   True
   False

2. The material used in magnetic storage devices is _____.

   a. copper
   b. steel
   c. iron
   d. nickel

3. A common use for the diskette is _____.

   a. moving files between computers
   b. loading new programs
   c. backing up data
   d. all of the above

4. Which diskette can hold more data?

   a. 5.25-inch diskette
   b. 3.5-inch diskette

5. Sectors form a noncontinuous spiral around the disk.

   True
   False

6. The location of all data is kept in a special _____ on the diskette.

   a. log
   b. folder
   c. journal
   d. sector

7. Removable hard disks are no different than the diskette except that they hold more.

   True
   False

8. Data on a tape drive is stored randomly like on the diskette.

   True
   False

9. CDs are read using a magnetic device.

   True
   False

10. The process that writes to a CD is known as _____.

    a. pitting
    b. burning
    c. logging
    d. organizing

11. The advantage of the Magneto-Optical drive is that the data can be written over like a diskette.

    True
    False

12. WORM stands for Write Often, Read Many.

    True
    False

13. The average access time is a combination of the speed at which a disk spins and the time it takes to move the heads from one track to another.

    True
    False

14. The data transfer rate is expressed as some amount of data per unit of space.

    True
    False

15. The first drives used the RLL encoding schemes.

    True
    False

16. SCSIs allow you to connect multiple peripheral devices.

    True
    False

CHAPTER 5
NETWORKS AND DATA COMMUNICATIONS

Directions

The Textnotes are a note taking and study aid.
- Fill in the Textnote blanks as you proceed through the software instruction.
- Any Textnote reference to computer commands such as "Click..." should be performed by you or your instructor, depending on the instructional setting.

Objectives

When you complete this chapter, you will be able to do the following:

- List four major benefits of connecting computers to form a network.
- Differentiate between a LAN and a WAN.
- Differentiate among file-server, client/server, and peer-to-peer computing.
- Describe the physical layout of networks based on bus, star, and ring topologies.
- Describe four common media for connecting the computers in a network.
- Compare the Ethernet, Token Ring and ARCnet protocols.
- Describe the most popular reasons for connecting computers through telephone lines.
- Explain how a modem works and what distinguishes one modem from another.
- List the most common types of digital lines and the basic characteristics of each.

The Uses Of A Network

A network is a way to connect computers together enabling them to communicate with one another, exchange information, and pool resources.

Simultaneous Access

Companies with multiple employees often use network versions of the most commonly used programs.

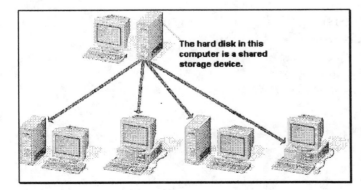

The hard disk in this computer is a shared storage device.

Some software designed for networks is classified as groupware.

This type of software includes:

- Scheduling and calendar software
- E-mail
- Document management

Shared Peripheral Devices

One way to link computers in a network is to share peripheral devices, such as laser printers, large
_____ _____ and _____.

Personal Communication

Electronic mail (e-mail) is a system for exchanging written messages through a
_____.

E-mail allows you to:

- share files (spreadsheets, documents).
- conduct teleconference and video conferencing.

Easier Backup

Networks can also be used to store critical _____.

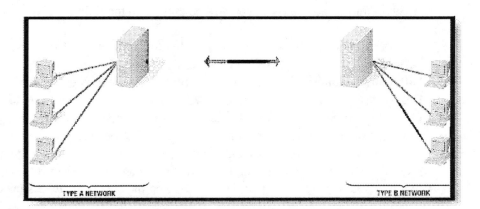

TYPE A NETWORK   TYPE B NETWORK

Categories Of Networks

Local Area Networks

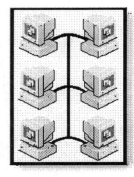

_____ _____ _____ (LAN) is a network of computers connected by a cable (or a small radio transmitter).

A LAN permits all connected computers to share:

- People (users)
- Data (information)
- Hardware (computers)
- Software (programs)

Connecting Networks

Connective networking is when two LANs are _____ together. A packet, also called frame, is a group of bits that includes a header and a payload. The payload contains the actual data being sent.

A _____ is a device that looks at the information in each packet header and rebroadcasts data traveling from one LAN to another.

A _____ is a device which acts as an electronic post office, sorting and sending data along the most expedient route to its destination.

A _____ is a computer system that connects two networks and translates one protocol into another.

Wide Area Networks

A _____ _____ _____(WAN) is two or more LANs that are connected together across a wide geographical area. The _____ is the ultimate WAN, since it connects many thousands of computers and LANs around the world.

File Server Networks

A file server network is an arrangement in which each node can have access to the files in the _____ but not necessarily to files on other nodes.

Client/Server Networks

A client/server network is an arrangement in which individual computers share the _____ and _____ workload with a central server.

Peer-to-Peer Computing

Peer-to-peer network allows distributed computing, which enables users to draw on the

_____

_____ of other computers in the network.

Network Topologies For LANs

_____ is the physical layout of the cables that connect the nodes of the network.

The Bus Topology

A bus network is a _____
_____ to which all the
network nodes and peripheral devices
are attached.

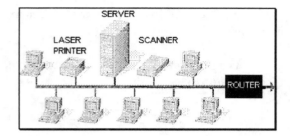

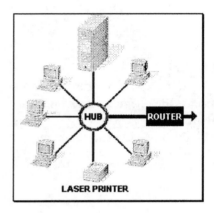

The Star Topology

A star network places a hub in the _____ of the
network node through which groups of data are routed.

The Ring Topology

The ring topology connects the nodes of the network in a
_____ chain through which data is sent.

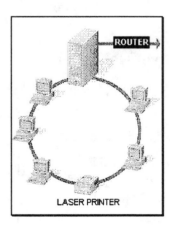

Network Media And Hardware

Twisted-Pair Wire

Twisted-pair wire consists of four to eight copper _____ individually insulated, then twisted and bound together in another layer of plastic _____.

Bandwidth is a form of _____ used to determine the amount of data a network media can transmit each second.

Unshielded twisted-pair (UTP) is _____ from outside interference by a plastic coating only.

Shielded twisted-pair (STP) is encased in a _____ sheath.

Coaxial Cable

Coaxial cable contains an _____ which is between one single wire and a wire mesh shield.

Fiber-Optic Cable

Fiber-optic cable is a thin strand of glass that _____ pulsating beams of light instead of electronic frequencies.

Wireless Links

Some uses of wireless communication in networks:

* Office LANs can use _____ signals to transmit data between nodes.
* _____ can be equipped with cellular telephones and a modem.
* WANs that cover long distances often use _____ and microwave communication.
* Corporate WANs connect two LANs using _____ transmission.

The Network Interface Card and Network Protocols

The network interface card (NIC) controls the _____ of data in each computer on the network. Network protocol is like a _____ computers use for communicating data.

Ethernet

_____, the most common network protocol, requires each computer or workstation on the network to take its turn when sending data.

Token Ring

Token ring is a protocol which transmits an electric token that travels in one direction visiting each _____ on the network until it reaches its destination.

ARCnet

Attached Resource Computer network (ARCnet) has both a topology and _____ all its own.

Network Software

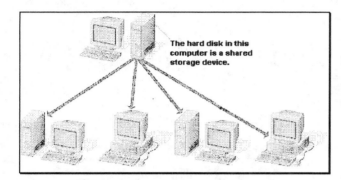

Network-operating system (NOS) is the group of _____ that manage the resources on the network.

Data Communication Over Telephone Lines

Telephone systems are now being accessed to transmit data communication onto computers through the phone lines.

Modems

How a Modem Works

A modem will translate _____ tones that travel over standard phone lines.

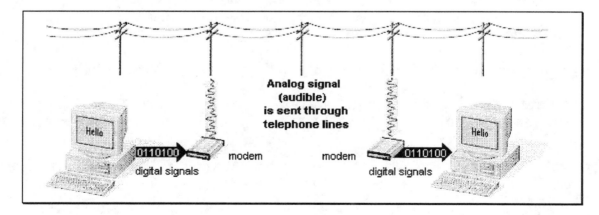

Choosing a Modem

Four areas to consider when buying a modem:

- Transmission speed or bits per second (bps)
- Data compression
- Error correction
- Internal versus external

An internal modem is a _____ _____ that plugs into one of the computer's expansion slots.

An external modem is a box that houses the modem's circuitry outside the computer.

Different forms of modems are:

- PC card
- standard phone lines
- cellular phone
- fax modem

Connecting with a Modem

Common uses for data communication over the phone lines:

- Direct connections with other users
- Connections with office LANs
- Connections with BBSs, online services, and the Internet

Direct Connections with Other Users

_____ _____ is the term used to describe sending a file to a remote computer. File-transfer protocol is the set of rules or guidelines that _____ the format in which data will be sent. Sending a file to another user or to a network is known as uploading the file.

Copying a file from a remote computer is known as downloading the file.

Full-duplex means that data can travel in both directions at the same time.

_____-_____ means that data can be sent in both directions but only one direction at a time.

Connections with Office Networks

Working at home or on the road and using telecommunications equipment is called _____.

Using Digital Telephone Lines

ISDN, T1, and T3

Integrated Services Digital Network (ISDN) is the best known _____ service offered by the phone company which replaces all _____ services with digital services.

Basic Rate ISDN (BRI) refers to a particular level of service that provides _____ channels on one line.

Primary Rate ISDN (PRI) is a higher level of service for ISDN that provides _____-_____ channels.

T1 (24 channels) and T3 (672 channels) are the different levels of _____.

ATM

Asynchronous Transfer Mode (ATM) is a _____ designed to send voice, video, and computer data over a single network.

The information superhighway is a _____ network capable of supporting high-bandwidth data communication to every home, school, and business.

Circuit-switched lines have a fixed amount of _____ available.

Packet-switched systems transmit packets of data.

ATM addresses the needs of different kinds of communication by providing different kinds of _____ and bandwidth on demand.

What To Expect In The Future

- Network technology to grow more sophisticated and _____ speeds to increase.
- Both the consumers of information and the telecommunications industry will work toward the goal of _____.
- Telecommunication _____ to work to offer high bandwidth to homes and businesses.

CHAPTER OUTLINE ACTIVITY

INSTRUCTIONS: The Chapter Outline Activity lists the instructional concepts and topics of this chapter in the order in which they appear. Fill in the outline's blanks with the correct word or phrase to better understand the chapter concepts. The number of blanks represent the number of words per response, while the length of the blanks do not represent the word length.

The Uses Of A Network

_____ Access

_____ Peripheral Devices
Personal Communication
Easier Backup

_____ Of Networks

_____ _____ _____

_____ - _____

_____ _____ _____

_____ _____ _____

_____ / _____ _____

Peer-to-Peer Computing

Network _____ For LANs

_____ _____ _____

_____ _____ _____

_____ _____ _____

Network Media And Hardware

_____ - _____ Wire

_____ Cable

_____ - _____ Cable
Wireless Links
The Network Interface Card and Network
   Protocols

_____

_____ _____

_____

Network Software

Data Communication Over Telephone Lines

Modems
How a Modem Works
Choosing a Modem
Connecting with a Modem
Direct Connections with Other Users
Connections with Office Networks

Digital Telephone Lines

_____, _____, and _____

_____

What To Expect In The Future

REVIEW QUESTIONS

1. E-mail is a type of software which is classified as _____.

    a. publicware
    b. groupware
    c. communicationware
    d. all of the above
    e. none of the above

2. Sharing peripheral devices such as laser printers is a way to link computers in a network.

    True
    False

3. _____ is a system for exchanging written messages through a network.

    a. Telnet
    b. E-mail
    c. Client/server
    d. All of the above
    e. None of the above

4. Networks can be used to store critical data.

    True
    False

5. In a LAN all the connected computers share _____.

    a. data
    b. hardware
    c. software
    d. all of the above
    e. none of the above

6. A router is a device that looks at the information in each packet header and rebroadcasts data traveling from one LAN to another.

    True
    False

7. A _____ is a computer system that connects two networks and translates one protocol into another.

   a.   gateway
   b.   router
   c.   bridge
   d.   all of the above
   e.   none of the above

8. The _____ is the ultimate WAN.

   a.   Internet
   b.   Telnet
   c.   ARCnet
   d.   all of the above
   e.   none of the above

9. A file server network connects two LANs together.

True
False

10. The client/server network _____.

   a.   is an arrangement in which individual computers share the processing and storage workload with a central server
   b.   is two or more LANs that are connected together across a wide geographical area
   c.   uses a strategy in which processing can be distributed among the various computers
   d.   allows distributed computing

11. Peer-to-peer _____.

   a.   is an arrangement in which individual computers share the processing and storage workload with a central server
   b.   is two or more LANs that are connected together across a wide geographical area
   c.   allows distributed computing, which enables users to draw on the processing power of other computers in the network
   d.   uses a hierarchical strategy for organizing networks

12. A bus network is a double conduit to which all the network nodes are attached.

True
False

13. _____ places a hub in the center of the network node through which groups of data are routed.

    a. Bus network
    b. Ring network
    c. Star network
    d. all of the above
    e. none of the above

14. Ring topology connects the nodes of the network in a _____ chain through which data is sent.

    a. straight
    b. boxed
    c. circular
    d. all of the above
    e. none of the above

15. Twisted-pair wire consists of four to eight copper strands.

True
False

16. _____ is a form of measurement used to determine the amount of data a network media can transmit each second.

    a. Datometer
    b. Bandwidth
    c. Compuscale
    d. All of the above
    e. None of the above

17. A coaxial cable contains _____ conductor(s).

    a. one
    b. two
    c. five
    d. all of the above
    e. none of the above

18. Not only is fiber-optic cable more expensive than twisted-pair wire, it is also more difficult to install.

True
False

19. _____ is a radio frequency in which wireless communication may use to transmit data between nodes.

   a. Ultraviolet light
   b. X-rays
   c. Microwaves
   d. All of the above
   e. None of the above

20. Network Interface Card or Network Protocols is a language computers use for communicating data.

   True
   False

21. Ethernet networks transmit an electronic token which travels to each node on the network.

   True
   False

22. Token Ring networks send data in a controlled manner in one direction only.

   True
   False

23. ARCnet stands for _____.

   a. Attached Resource Computer network
   b. Area Resource Circuit network
   c. Available Ring Computer network
   d. all of the above
   e. none of the above

24. Network-operating systems are groups of programs that manage the resources on the network.

   True
   False

25. Using the telephone systems for data communication is an alternative to using dedicated media.

   True
   False

26. A modem will translate _____ tones.

    a. high-pitched
    b. ear deaf
    c. word
    d. all of the above
    e. none of the above

27. A circuit board is an example of a(n) _____.

    a. fax modem insert
    b. internal modem
    c. external modem
    d. all of the above
    e. none of the above

28. A computer equipped with a modem and connected to a standard telephone line can communicate with any other computer even if they don't have a modem.

True
False

29. Copying a file from a remote computer is known as _____.

    a. uploading
    b. transferring
    c. downloading
    d. all of the above
    e. none of the above

30. Modem communication is normally full-duplex.

True
False

31. These days, more and more people are telecommuting.

True
False

32. The best known digital service is called _____, which replaces analog phone lines.

    a. digitized
    b. ISDN
    c. DSC
    d. all of the above
    e. none of the above

33. A T3 line offers _____ lines.

    a. 3
    b. 13
    c. 672
    d. 686

34. ISDN is also best suited for transmitting live video and sound.

    True
    False

35. Circuit-switched lines _____.

    a. are citywide networks capable of supporting low-bandwidth data to local businesses
    b. have a fixed amount of bandwidth available
    c. transmit packets of data
    d. all of the above
    e. none of the above

CHAPTER 6
THE OPERATING SYSTEM AND THE USER INTERFACE

Directions

The Textnotes are a note taking and study aid.
- Fill in the Textnote blanks as you proceed through the software instruction.
- Any Textnote reference to computer commands such as "Click…" should be performed by you or your instructor, depending on the instructional setting.

Objectives

When you complete this chapter, you will be able to do the following:

- Define operating system.
- Explain the importance of the user interface.
- Discuss other major functions of the operating system, such as managing hardware and managing files.
- Understand how utility software supports the operating system.
- Define multitasking and explain how it saves time for a user.
- Review the important Microsoft operating systems, starting with MS-DOS.
- List other significant operating systems, such as the Macintosh operating system, UNIX, and OS/2.

What Is An Operating System?

The operating system interprets instructions from the user and manages the tasks performed by the computer.

The OS performs the following functions:

- Provides instructions to display the user interface onto the screen.
- _____ programs into the computer's memory for use.
- Coordinates how programs work with the _____.
- Manages the way information is stored on and retrieved from _____.

The User Interface

Parts of the Interface

The Desktop
The desktop displays _____, which are pictures similar to what you would find on a desk. The interface is often called a graphical user interface (GUI), or the point-and-click interface.

Icons
Icons are the _____ on-screen that represent parts of the computer with which you work. Remember these rules when you use a mouse to interact with the icons.

- Clicking an icon highlights, or activates, the icon.
- A highlighted icon is said to be selected so that you can act on it, such as by copying or deleting it.
- Notice that the My Computer icon has now been selected.

The Taskbar and the Start Button

The taskbar is the area of the Desktop where the **Start** button and clock are located.

Active programs are highlighted on the **taskbar**.

Programs Running in Windows
Across the top of a window is the _____ _____. This area displays the name of the application, document, or device which the window represents.

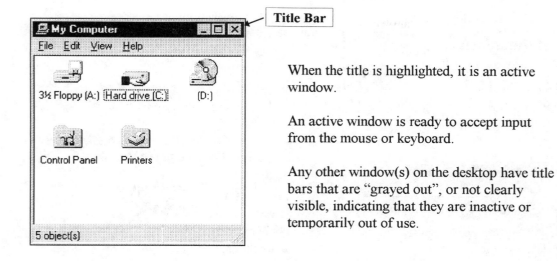

Title Bar

When the title is highlighted, it is an active window.

An active window is ready to accept input from the mouse or keyboard.

Any other window(s) on the desktop have title bars that are "grayed out", or not clearly visible, indicating that they are inactive or temporarily out of use.

Scroll bars are used to view parts of the program or file that are longer or wider than what can be displayed. A scroll bar appears along the right or bottom side of a window when there is not enough room to display the window's contents.

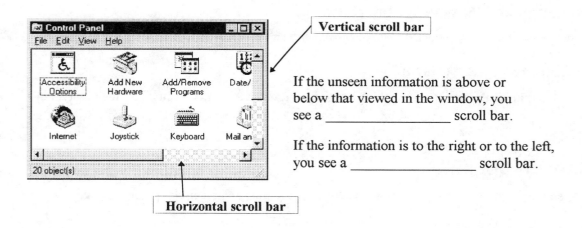

Vertical scroll bar

If the unseen information is above or below that viewed in the window, you see a _____ scroll bar.

If the information is to the right or to the left, you see a _____ scroll bar.

Horizontal scroll bar

Window Control Buttons

In Windows 95, 3 buttons in the title bar allow you to _____ the window's size.

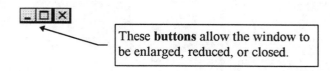

These **buttons** allow the window to be enlarged, reduced, or closed.

In Windows 3.1 and others, the same manipulation functions are available but represented differently.

Menus

The menu bar contains the names of menus you can use within a window. Clicking a menu name, such as File, displays its menu options.

Dialog Boxes

Dialog boxes are the special-purpose boxes which appear when you need to tell the program what to do next.

Clicking this **button** displays a drop-down list of options.

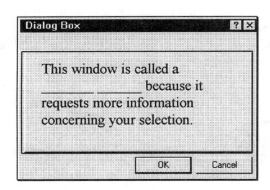

The list remains on-screen until you click an option to choose it or click outside the list to cancel the display.

Becoming Familiar with the Interface

Common user access (CUA) is the level of consistency in the _____.

The Command-Line Interface

Prior to the graphical user interface, users would interact with a command-line interface by typing strings of _____ at the appearance of a prompt on-screen.

Running Programs

The operating system provides an interface between programs and other computer resources.

Sharing Information

Throughout Windows 95, each application's Edit menu has three consistent Clipboard commands: Cut, Copy, and Paste.

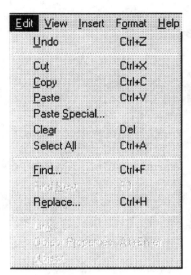

Cut places a replica of the selected object into the Clipboard and removes it from its original location.

Copy places a replica of the selected object into the Clipboard and leaves the original alone.

Paste inserts the contents of the Clipboard onto the active location, such as the insertion point in a text file or the Contents pane in the Exploring window.

Two features of the Clipboard:

- Object Embedding
- Object Linking
- Object Linking and Embedding

Multitasking

Multitasking is performing two or more procedures at the same time. Two methods of multitasking:

- _____ Multitasking
- _____ Multitasking

Managing Files

To store information efficiently, in the form of files, you tell the operating system:

- On which drive to store the file.
- In which folder to put the file.
- By what name to identify the file.
- By what type to create the file.

File names consist of two primary parts:

- File Name - a descriptive name that a user assigns to a _____ file.
- Extension - follows the name and specifies the _____ of data in the file.

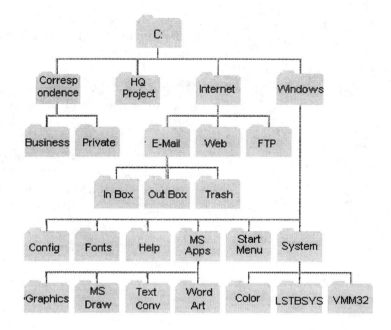

The hierarchical-file system is used to organize the many folders and files.

Managing Hardware

The _____ _____ serves as the mediator between programs and hardware.

Processing Interrupts

The operating system:

- _____ commands to use memory and other devices.
- keeps track of which programs have access to which devices.
- coordinates everything the _____ does to keep the order in which it was received.

Providing Drivers

Drivers allow various programs to activate and use the hardware device.

Networking

Networking is working with multiple computers on the network.

Enhancing The Operating System With Utility Software

Utilities are programs used to improve operating systems.

File Defragmentation

A file that has been added to is called a fragmented file. A _____ program that defragments files will speed up the disk drive.

Data Compression

Data compression is used to fit more data on a disk. Data compression utilities can either _____ files on demand or _____ all the data on a hard disk drive.

Backup Software

Backup software helps _____ large groups of files from your hard disk to another storage media.

Data Recovery Software

Data recovery utilities will recover data files that have been mistakenly _____.

Antivirus Utilities

Antivirus utilities _____ the boot sector and every file on a disk attempting to remove any viruses.

Screen Savers

Originally, the screen saver was used to _____ images from being "burned" into the screen.

Microsoft Operating Systems

MS-DOS

Microsoft's MS-DOS was once the most common of all the PC operating systems. Limitations of DOS:

- Only one program can be loaded into _____ at a time.
- Not designed to handle large amounts of _____ that today's PCs use.
- Works at low speeds.
- _____ have a limited number of characters.

Microsoft Windows 3.0, 3.1, and 3.11

Microsoft Windows replaced the command-line interface with a point-and-click operating environment. Windows has the ability to load more than one program into _____ at a time.

Microsoft Windows 95 (and Upgrades)

Windows 95 is a complete operating system and a successor to DOS for desktop computers. Features:

- Designed to run _____-_____ applications, with the ability to run older 16-bit applications.
- Preemptive _____ operating system.
- _____ interface.
- Compatible with _____ software.

Microsoft Windows NT

Windows NT is a _____-_____ operating system designed for powerful workstations and network servers.

Other Operating Systems For Personal Computers

The Macintosh Operating System

A purely _____ machine. All of its applications function _____, making them easier to learn than DOS.

Features include built-in _____ and plug-and-play hardware compatibility.

OS/2

The OS/2 is a _____-_____ multitasking operating system with a point-and-click interface.

UNIX

UNIX serves as a model for PC operating systems. It is a multi-user and multiprocessing operating system. One of its disadvantages is the many _____ needed to do even the simple things.

Norton Workshop: Multitasking And OLE

In the following steps we will see the operating system and Object Linking and Embedding (OLE) used to create a linked summary containing text and spreadsheet data. In addition, multitasking will be used the entire time, because a CD will be playing during the process.

Begin in the Windows 95 desktop and locate the CD Player in the Start menu.

- Launch the CD Player.
- Place the CD in the CD-ROM drive.
- Click on the play button.

Locate the file that contains the text for the summary page by opening the Window Explorer.

Select Find Files or Folders from the Tools menu to display the Find: All Files dialog box.

- Enter the file name (Summary 1, Wk 1)
- Click on the Find Now button

Navigate to the spreadsheet file using the Explorer to obtain the data needed for the text. Highlight the data which will be linked from the spreadsheet and choose Copy from the Edit menu.

Go back to the text document and move the cursor to the place where we will want to Paste the linked data. It is important to select the Paste Link option and select Microsoft Excel Worksheet Object.

Click on OK to paste the data into the text document. Save the document with a new name, in a new folder.

Navigate to the Research folder and click on Create New Folder button. Name the new folder then move to the new folder.

Enter the new file name as Summary Wk.1. Complete by clicking Save As in the dialog box. Exit the spreadsheet software and the word processing program.

Push the Stop button on the CD player and remove the CD. To turn off the computer, select Shut Down from the Start menu.

What To Expect In The Future

- Technologies just beginning to emerge are likely to become standard parts of future _____ _____.

- Changes in the _____ of the operating system will occur while it remains the most important program in the computer.

CHAPTER OUTLINE ACTIVITY

INSTRUCTIONS: The Chapter Outline Activity lists the instructional concepts and topics of this chapter in the order in which they appear. Fill in the outline's blanks with the correct word or phrase to better understand the chapter concepts. The number of blanks represent the number of words per response, while the length of the blanks do not represent the word length.

What Is An Operating System?

The User Interface
Parts of the Interface

_____ _____

_____

The Taskbar and the Start Button

_____ _____ ___ _____

Window _____ Buttons

_____

_____ Boxes

Becoming Familiar with the _____

The _____ - _____ Interface

Running Programs
Sharing Information

_____

Managing Files

Managing Hardware
Processing Interrupts
Providing Drivers

_____

Enhancing The Operating System With Utility Software

_____ _____

Data Compression

_____ Software

Data Recovery Software

_____ _____

_____ _____

Microsoft Operating Systems

____ - _____

Microsoft Windows 3.0, 3.1, 3.11

_____ _____ _____
 (and Upgrades)

Microsoft Windows NT

Other Operating Systems For Personal Computers
The Macintosh Operating System

_____ / ____

_____

Norton Workshop: Multitasking And OLE

What To Expect In The Future

REVIEW QUESTIONS

1. An operating system is similar to other computer programs.

   True
   False

2. The _____ is the part of the operating system that the user sees.

   a. keyboard
   b. desktop
   c. user interface
   d. all of the above
   e. none of the above

3. A graphical user interface is also called a _____ interface.

   a. point-and-click
   b. picture-perfect
   c. graphic
   d. all of the above
   e. none of the above

4. _____ are symbols which represent printers, fonts, document files, and disk drives.

   a. Drivers
   b. Objects
   c. Icons
   d. all of the above
   e. none of the above

5. The purpose of the _____ is to hold and display the buttons for the programs which are running.

   a. menu bar
   b. taskbar
   c. title bar
   d. all of the above
   e. none of the above

6. The active program is represented as a highlighted button in the taskbar.

   True
   False

7. The title bar is positioned at the _____ of the window.

    a. bottom
    b. end
    c. top
    d. all of the above
    e. none of the above

8. _____ bars view the different parts of the programs that are not able to be displayed because of the length or width of the data.

    a. Scroll
    b. Title
    c. Inactive
    d. All of the above
    e. None of the above

9. Menu buttons are used to manipulate the size of the windows.

    True
    False

10. One way to start a task is to choose commands from lists called _____.

    a. menus
    b. control panels
    c. starters
    d. all of the above
    e. none of the above

11. A dialog box displays the buttons for the programs you are running.

    True
    False

12. The level of consistency in the interface is an important part of making the computer system intuitive and easy to use.

    True
    False

13. The command-line interface is much like the graphical user interface.

    True
    False

14. A _____ is a temporary storage space for data that is being copied or moved.

    a. clipboard
    b. memory bank
    c. post office
    d. all of the above
    e. none of the above

15. When object embedding takes place, data retains a link to the original document.

    True
    False

16. Cooperative multitasking allows a user to print while continuing to type or use the mouse to input more data.

    True
    False

17. The Window Explorer is a program used for viewing and managing the contents of a disk.

    True
    False

18. The operating system uses interrupt requests to help the _____ coordinate processes.

    a. hard disk
    b. CPU
    c. other hardware
    d. all of the above
    e. none of the above

19. _____ are complete programs for working with special devices, such as printers.

    a. Platforms
    b. Utilities
    c. Drivers
    d. All of the above
    e. None of the above

20. _____ is a system of interconnected computers that can communicate with each other and share applications and data.

    a. Share-tasking
    b. Cooperative multitasking
    c. Networking
    d. All of the above
    e. None of the above

21. A fragmented file is easy for the hard drive to read.

    True
    False

22. Data compression techniques are built into modems so they can send files faster.

    True
    False

23. Backing up software should be done by all users.

    True
    False

24. A data recovery utility can also be called a(n) _____.

    a. unerase program
    b. find program
    c. hidden program
    d. all of the above
    e. none of the above

25. A virus is a parasitic program buried within another legitimate program or stored in an area called the boot sector.

    True
    False

26. A screen saver is a plastic shield that is used to cover the screen on a computer when it is not in use.

    True
    False

27. DOS was formerly the most popular operating system.

    True
    False

28. Windows was originally not an operating system but an operating environment.

    True
    False

29. Windows 95 allows users to type file names of up to _____ characters.

    a. 16
    b. 32
    c. 256
    d. all of the above
    e. none of the above

30. Windows NT was originally designed to be the successor to DOS.

    True
    False

31. The _____ has long been a favorite among GUI fans and people who use high-powered graphics and publishing applications.

    a. IBM
    b. Macintosh
    c. UNIX
    d. all of the above
    e. none of the above

32. OS/2 is not a point-and-click interface.

    True
    False

33. UNIX is a multi-user and multiprocessing operating system.

    True
    False

CHAPTER 7
WORD PROCESSING AND DESKTOP PUBLISHING

Directions

The Textnotes are a note taking and study aid.
- Fill in the Textnote blanks as you proceed through the software instruction.
- Any Textnote reference to computer commands such as "Click…" should be performed by you or your instructor, depending on the instructional setting.

Objectives

When you complete this chapter, you will be able to do the following:

- Describe the types of documents you can create with word processing software.
- Discuss the editing and formatting features of word processing software.
- Explain the purpose of HTML editing, the mail merge feature, style sheets, and the Print Preview window.
- Explain the difference between word processing and desktop publishing programs.
- Describe some of the important features of desktop publishing software.

The Many Uses Of Word Processing Software

Word processing software gives the user powerful tools with which to enter and manipulate text to produce:

- Simple notes and memos
- Brochures
- Resumes
- Lengthy reports

Your Window Into The Document

The screen that appears when you first launch a word processor is usually the main editing screen.

This is simply a window through which you can view your documents as you _____ and _____ them. Most word processors display documents in a _____ that closely resembles what the printed document will look like.
This feature is called WYSIWYG (pronounced "wiz-ee-wig") and is an acronym for _____
_____ _____ _____ _____ _____ _____.

Entering Text

Text is entered through the keyboard, beginning in the _____ _____ _____ of a new document.

Word Wrap

Word processing software is filled with _____ saving features.

One of the most common is called word wrap. If a word at the _____ _____ of a line is too long to fit on that line, the program will move it to the _____ of the next line.

This is done automatically and does not require the user to hit _____.

This allows the user to type continuously without having to worry about hitting Enter at the end of each line thus saving time.

Navigating Around a Document

Often documents are longer than what can appear in the word processor's screen or window at one time.

When you are typing and get to the bottom of the screen, the text moves up to make room for more text to be entered. This movement is called _____, a term that comes from the concept of a continuous scroll of paper.

Scrolling through a document can be achieved by using the _____ _____ _____. Another way of moving through a document is by the use of the _____ _____. The scroll bar is a _____ _____ on the _____ _____ of the screen or window.

Scroll Bar

At the top and bottom of the scroll bar are two buttons with small arrows on them.

Scroll Arrows

Scroll Box

These buttons are called _____ _____. Clicking on the corresponding arrow causes the document to scroll up or down.

Within the scroll bar is a _____ _____ called a _____ _____. The scroll box shows your approximate _____ in a document relative to its overall length. Moving the scroll box to the center of the scroll bar would take you to the _____ of the document.

Likewise, moving the scroll box to the bottom of the scroll bar would take you to the _____ of the document.

Clicking on the scroll bar _____ or _____ the scroll box will move you one page up or down respectively.

Editing Text

Perhaps the greatest advantage provided by word processors is the ability to _____ _____ on a page without retyping the whole page.

Changing an existing document is called _____ the document.

Correcting a Typing Mistake

There are several ways to correct a typing mistake. If the error occurs immediately prior to the cursor's location, use the _____ _____ to erase and retype the word.

Sometimes a mistake is found well after it was first typed.

Using the backspace key is impractical because it would erase everything after the mistake as well.

In this situation, you could use either the _____ _____ or the _____ to place the cursor after the mistake. Once the cursor is on the misspelled word, you can use the _____ _____ to erase and retype it.

Selecting Blocks

Sometimes it is necessary to edit a large section, or _____
text you must first mark it. This marking process is called

Most programs allow you to select text by _____
_____ the cursor to the end of the desired
change color along with the background. The text then sa

Sometimes it is necessary to edit a large section, or _____, of text. To work with a block of text, you must first mark it. This marking process is called _____.

Most programs allow you to select text by _____ at the beginning and _____ the cursor to the end of the desired block. Doing so causes the text to change color along with the background. The text then is said to be _____.

Working with Blocks of Text

Once a block of text is selected, it can be:

- deleted (cut)
- copied and pasted
- moved

Some word processors allow you to move text by _____ on a selected block of text and _____ it wherever you want.

This function is called _____ _____ _____ _____.

Find and Replace

_____ and _____ (find and change) allows you to search an entire document for each occurrence of a word and replace it with another word.

The Undo Command

Sometimes in the process of editing, you will make a mistake, for example deleting a large block of text accidentally.

Most word processors will allow you to _____ your mistake and _____ the document as it was prior to the error.

Another way to avoid the danger of a big editing mistake is to _____ often.

By doing so, you will always have a recent version of the document prior to the mistake. Periodic saving also prevents the loss of data due to _____ _____ or _____.

Checking Spelling

Another very useful tool provided by most word processors is the _____ _____.

A spelling checker compares each word of a document to its _____ and alerts you to any _____ _____.

Most good spelling checkers will offer possible alternatives to the misspelled word.

Sometimes words, like _____ _____, are not in the spelling checker's dictionary.

Often these words can be added to a _____ _____ that can be tailored to your personal needs.

The draw back to spelling checkers is that they will not detect _____ _____ or _____ _____ that result in actual words.

To help locate these types of errors, some word processors provide a grammar checker. This tool can check for _____ _____, _____ _____, and sometimes even _____ _____.

Using a Thesaurus

The computerized thesaurus has been a tool provided by word processors almost as long as the spelling checker.

It is very useful for suggesting _____ _____ when a word you have used doesn't quite fit the document being composed.

Formatting Text

Most of the features in word processing software are designed for controlling:

- the appearance of text
- the layout of the page
- the inclusion of pictures and other graphics

Character Formats

Fonts
The term font (or _____) refers to the style of the letters, symbols, and punctuation marks in your document.

There are literally hundreds of fonts, but they all fall into two general categories:

- Monospace
- Proportional

In a monospace font, every character takes up exactly the same amount of horizontal space.

```
This is the Courier font, which is monospaced.
This is the Arial font, which is proportional.
```

The most common monospace font is _____.

Most fonts, however, are _____.

This means that each letter does not necessarily take up the _____ amount of _____ space.

For example, the capitol letters M and I take up very different amounts of space because the __ is wider than the ____.

Fonts also fall into two other broad categories:

- Serif
- Sans serif

_____ typefaces have fancy curls and extra decorative strokes on each character; _____ _____ fonts do not (Sans means "without" in French).

_____ _____ are generally more readable and are therefore better for body text.

_____ _____ _____ lend themselves much better to headings or display text.

Type Size

This is 10 point Times New Roman type.
This is 12 point Times New Roman type.
This is 14 point Times New Roman type.
This is 16 point Times New Roman type.
This is 18 point Times New Roman type.
This is 24 point Times New Roman type.
This is 36 point Times New Roman type.

The size of a font is measured in _____ which are equal to .02 inches each in height.

The most common size used in business documents is 12-point type and is .17 inch tall.

This measurement is from the _____ of the tallest letters to the _____ of the letters that descend below the baseline (g, j, p, q, and y).

Types Styles

The most common type styles are:

- bold
- italics
- underlined

- strike through
- small caps
- large caps

Applying Character Formats to Your Document

Formatting of text can happen before or after the text is entered. Both methods are common.

One thing to remember is that _____ is usually better. Too many character formats can make a document look _____ or _____.

Paragraph Formats

In word processing, the word _____ has a slightly different meaning than it does traditionally.

Simply put, every time the _____ _____ is pressed a new paragraph is created.

Therefore, a group of _____ can be a paragraph but so can a two word _____.

Line and Paragraph Spacing

The distance between _____ _____ of printed text is called line spacing. Line spacing can be:

- single spaced
- double spaced
- custom spaced (which can be any spacing you desire)

_____ _____ refers to the distance between paragraphs.

The paragraph spacing usually defaults to the _____ _____, but can be changed to suit the needs of the user.

Indents and Alignment

In a word processing document, the _____ are the white borders around the edge of the page where there is no text.

Margins, once set, prevent text from spilling over to the edges of the page.

Indents determine how close the first line of a _____ comes to the _____.

Alignment refers to the _____ of the lines of a paragraph with respect to the _____.

There are four possible alignments of text:

- Right
- Left
- Center
- Justified (or full justified)

Tabs and Tab Stops

The keyboard's _____ _____ moves the cursor forward (to the right) on the screen to the next tab stop.

A tab stop is a _____, both on-screen and in the document, usually measured from the left margin.

Tab stops are commonly measured in _____ _____ or inches.

Most word processors have default tab stops every _____ _____, or every _____, but can easily be changed.

Tabs are most often used to accurately align columns of text. Four common tab stops are:

- the left-aligned tab stop
- the right-aligned tab stop
- the centered tab stop
- the decimal tab stop

Borders and Shading

A border, often called a _____, is a line that is drawn on one or more sides of a paragraph.

Shading draws a _____ color or _____ around a paragraph.

Both borders and shading are effective tools for setting a paragraph off and drawing special attention to it.

Document Formats

One of the most important document formats is the _____ _____, which was described under indents and alignment.

Often setting the margins is the first step in formatting a new document.

Page Size and Orientation

Most printed documents are set up to fit on 8.5 by 11-inch paper. However, you can set your document format to other standard paper sizes, such as _____ _____ (8.5 by 14 inches).

The dimensions of a document can also be determined by the _____ of the paper.

There are two settings for page orientation:

- Portrait orientation
- Landscape orientation

Headers, Footers, and Footnotes

Headers and footers are lines of text that appear at the _____ and _____ of a page in long documents.

Often, they contain such information as a _____ _____ and the _____ _____ _____ _____. Other information that might also be included in a header or footer is the name of the author and the _____ of printing.

A footnote should not be confused with a _____.

Footnotes are designed to give _____ _____ to what is in the main body of text.

Word processors will often include tools for _____ and _____ footnotes.

Advanced Word Processing Features

Print Preview

Many word processors allow you to view an entire page or facing pages on the screen before they are printed.

This feature is called print preview.

Print preview is a useful tool for seeing how overall formatting characteristics, such as _____ _____, _____, and _____ will affect the appearance of your document.

Mail Merge

Another useful tool provided with many word processors is mail merge. This tool allows you to combine a _____ _____ with a _____ _____ to produce individually addressed letters.

Using mail merge saves time by enabling you to type a letter once and then automatically _____ the correct names and addresses into the document.

Adding HTML Codes to Make World Wide Web Pages

The rise in popularity of the _____ _____ _____ in recent years has led many companies and individuals to create documents that are accessible electronically.

These documents are called _____ _____ and are created with a formatting code known as _____ _____ _____ (_____).

Today, some word processors come equipped with the ability to format documents using HTML, so they can be turned into Web pages.

Adding Graphics and Sounds

Adding graphics and sounds can greatly enhance a document's impact, so many word processing applications make it very easy to add them.

Most word processors can import standard types of graphic files that can then be:

- moved
- sized
- cropped
- enhanced with borders

Text can even be aligned around a picture. _____ _____ are attached in much the same way as a graphic.

The difference is that an _____, often a speaker functioning as a _____ _____, is placed in the document.

Styles and Style Sheets

A style is a named collection of _____ and _____ formats.

A style named Plain Text might include the following formatting settings:

- Times, 12-point
- Left alignment
- Double-spacing

A style sheet is a collection of styles that can be applied to a group of similar documents.

Once a style is set up, it can be _____ _____ by simply selecting it from a menu. This saves time when a document is long and filled with lots of repetitive elements like

_____.

Style sheets can also save time if _____ _____ need to be made to a document.

If you decide to change the font of the headings in a document, simply changing the style's _____ ____ _____ _____

changes all the headings automatically.

Style dialog box:

Styles:
- ¶ List Number 4
- ¶ List Number 5
- ¶ Part Label
- ¶ Part Subtitle
- ¶ Picture
- Section Heading
- ¶ Signature

List:
All Styles

Paragraph Preview

Character Preview
Arial

Description
Heading 1+

Apply
Cancel
New
Modify
Delete

Desktop Publishing Software

The publishing and graphic arts industries were revolutionized by the introduction of
_____ _____ (_____)_____ to the PC market.

This technology gives the ordinary user the power to produce professional publications with relative ease.

What was once a _____ and _____ process involving many different people with _____ _____, can now be accomplished by one person with just a PC and a printer.

Even within the publishing industry itself, DTP software is used to increase:

- efficiency
- production capacity
- profits

Desktop Publishing Versus Word Processing

As desktop publishing and word processing programs have grown more _____, the line between them has blurred.

Word processing software now often includes capabilities that were once exclusively found in DTP software like the _____ _____.

DTP applications also now include such features as:

- find and replace
- spell checking

Though the lines continue to blur, DTP is still the best choice for:

- professional-quality typesetting and page layout
- making sophisticated use of graphics and color
- commercial-quality printing

Type Controls

In addition to the type controls that are found in word processors, DTP software provides two more essential tools:

- Kerning
- Tracking

_____ allows you to make fine adjustments of the _____ between individual letters in a word.

For example, you might move a capital _____ and a capital _____ closer together because they look too far apart.

You might also add space between an _____ and an _____; because, together, they can look like a letter m if they are too close.

_____ also adjusts _____ _____, but rather than making adjustments between individual characters, entire _____ _____ _____ are changed.

Other special text controls include:

- drop caps
- initial caps
- rotated text

Graphics Controls

Desktop publishing software includes greater sophistication in the realm of _____ _____ than does word processing software.

DTP programs provide more direct control over the exact placement of _____, _____ _____ _____ options, and the incorporation of _____.
Other graphics controls exclusive to DTP software include:

- applying color to a black-and-white or gray image
- linking graphics to text elements
- adjusting brightness, contrast, and halftone screens
- making negative images of imported graphics
- selecting color models on which to base color adjustments

Page Layout and Document Controls

Desktop publishing programs include more sophisticated controls for setting up the _____ of documents.

One of the most common elements for page layout in DTP software is called _____ _____. These are special pages within the document that are set aside for defining elements common to all pages in the document, such as:

- Page numbers
- Headers and footers
- Ruling lines
- Margin features
- Special graphics
- Layout guides

Having all these elements on one master page allows you to make adjustments to them with respect to the entire page.

DTP master pages also provide an easy way to create _____.

Templates are _____ _____ that are ready for text to be inserted quickly and easily.

Prepress Controls

Perhaps the most unique feature of DTP software is the ability to prepare documents for the _____ _____.

If color is used in a document, DTP software is essential for press preparation. DTP software allows colors to be specified according to industry standards, such as:

- Pantone
- TruMatch

This avoids any confusion between you and the printer.

Documents to be printed in color must have

_____

created for each color on each page. These pages are called _____

_____.

The two main types of color separations are:

- spot color separations
- process color separations

Spot color separation prints a _____ _____ for items in a particular color.

This method is a good way to save money if you are printing a document that is mostly _____ _____ _____ but contains one additional _____.

Process color separations are created when _____ _____ printing is required.

One separation is printed for each page in each of the three primary printing colors _____(blue), _____(red), and _____, as well as _____. This is called CMYK separation.

DTP software also allows you to utilize _____ _____ and registration marks (or targets) for page and color separation alignment.

_____ show precisely where the corners of the page are, and _____ allow precise alignment of color separations.

Some DTP programs also have controls for _____. This is the process of adding a tiny overlap to _____ _____ _____ on a page to account for possible _____ in the press.

One last advantage of DTP programs is their ability to create _____ _____ for printing to digital image setters.

These are used by the printer to create _____ for the press without requiring the intermediate step of a _____ _____.

In this process, _____ _____ is exposed by a laser which produces a higher-quality product than that of a _____ _____.

Norton Workshop: Creating A Professional Memo

The memo is an informal, yet efficient, means of communicating with colleagues in the business world.

To get a sense of the process of creating a memo with word processing software, read along as Marilyn puts one together. Marilyn is accustomed to using many templates. She decides to browse through the ones offered with the software.

After viewing the other choices, she settles on the "Elegant Memo." She double-clicks on the template, and a new, untitled file appears.

Marilyn wants to change the format slightly, but it is usually better to enter the content before worrying about formatting. She enters the information into the template. After reviewing her work, Marilyn makes a few changes to the memo. Using drag-and-drop editing, she moves the first sentence after the second.

Next, she uses the spell checker to be sure that no words are misspelled. There are no mistakes, so she moves on to formatting the document.

Double-clicking on the word "Memo" selects it for editing. She then chooses Font from the Format menu, which brings up the dialog box.

From here, she can select many different font options and view each of them in the Preview window. She finally settles on 9 pt., Arial Narrow, bold, blue.

With all the character settings completed, she clicks on OK and returns to the main editing screen.

Marilyn wants to include a picture of the guest speaker for the upcoming event. She chooses Picture from the Insert menu and selects the picture to insert into the document.

Next, she inserts a table into the memo to provide sales information on several different products.

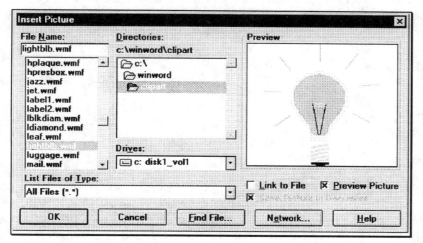

Lastly, she decides to include a piece of her favorite clip art. Clip art consists of small images that are often included with software. She again selects Picture from the Insert menu and browses through the many pieces of clip art available. She chooses a graphic file called Lightbulb.wmf and previews it in the viewing window.

After clicking OK to verify her selection, the graphic appears in the memo. Satisfied with her work, Marilyn prints a copy of the finished document.

What To Expect In The Future

As programs grow in _____ and _____, the lines between word processors and DTP software will continue to blur.

This can lead to the problem known as "_____." That is, software that gets bigger and bigger (and more expensive) even though most users employ only a small part of the program's overall ability.

One solution to this problem is the trend towards a more _____ approach to large applications. In this approach, large applications are broken down into _____, _____ _____ parts which are sold separately.

This allows the user to decide what is required and purchase only those modules, thus avoiding the expense of unused functionality.

CHAPTER OUTLINE ACTIVITY

INSTRUCTIONS: The Chapter Outline Activity lists the instructional concepts and topics of this chapter in the order in which they appear. Fill in the outline's blanks with the correct word or phrase to better understand the chapter concepts. The number of blanks represent the number of words per response, while the length of the blanks do not represent the word length.

The Many Uses Of Word Processing Software

Your Window Into The Document

Entering Text

_____ _____

_____ _____ _ _____

Editing Text

_____ __ Typing _____

_____ _____

_____ ____ _____ __ Text

_____ ___ _____

____ _____ Command

_____ _____

Using __ _____

Formatting Text
Character Formats

_____

_____ _____

_____ _____

Applying Character Formats to Your Document

Paragraph Formats
Line and Paragraph Spacing

_____ and Alignment

_____ and ____ Stops
Borders and Spacing

Document Formats
Page Size and Orientation
Headers, Footers, and Footnotes

Advanced Word Processing Features
Print Preview
Mail Merge
Adding HTML Codes to Make World Wide Web Pages

Adding _____ and _____
Styles and Style Sheets

Desktop Publishing Software
Desktop Publishing Versus Word Processing

_____ _____

_____ _____

____ _____ ___ _____ _____

Prepress _____

Norton Workshop: Creating A Professional Memo

What To Expect In The Future

REVIEW QUESTIONS

1. Most word processors display documents in a _____ that closely resembles what the printed document will look like.

   a. text format
   b. graphical format
   c. digital format
   d. logical format

2. Word wrap does not save the user much time.

   True
   False

3. You can move around a document using the:

   a. cursor-movement keys.
   b. scroll bar.
   c. neither A nor B.
   d. both A and B.

4. Changing an existing document is called _____ the document.

   a. proofing
   b. reviewing
   c. editing
   d. modifying

5. The best method for correcting a mistake found well after it was typed is to use the backspace key.

   True
   False

6. A large section of text is called a:

   a. block.
   b. chunk.
   c. paragraph.
   d. string.

7. Once a block of text is selected, it can be:

   a. deleted.
   b. copied and pasted.
   c. moved.
   d. all of the above.

8. Find and Replace and Find and Change mean the same thing.

   True
   False

9. A good way to avoid data loss due to power loss or surges is to save often.

   True
   False

10. A _____ checks for misspelled words and offers possible alternatives.

   a. thesaurus
   b. custom dictionary
   c. grammar checker
   d. spell checker

11. A spell checker is an excellent tool for locating word usage mistakes.

   True
   False

12. A _____ is a good tool for providing an alternative word for your document.

   a. thesaurus
   b. custom dictionary
   c. grammar checker
   d. spell checker

13. The term _____ refers to the style of the letters, symbols, and punctuation marks in your document.

   a. serif
   b. font
   c. type
   d. sans serif

14. _____ typefaces have fancy curls and extra decorative strokes on each character.

   a. Serif
   b. Sans serif
   c. Monospace
   d. Proportional

15. The most common monospace font is:

   a. Arial.
   b. Times New Roman.
   c. Courier.
   d. Palatino.

16. The most common size used in business documents is 12-point type.

   True
   False

17. When applying character formats to your documents, using more is usually better.

   True
   False

18. Every time the _____ is pressed a new paragraph is created.

   a. space bar
   b. tab key
   c. shift key
   d. return key

19. Line spacing can be:

   a. single spaced.
   b. double spaced.
   c. custom spaced.
   d. all of the above.

20. Alignment determines how close the first line of a paragraph comes to the margin.

   True
   False

21. Tab stops are commonly measured in:

    a.   character width.
    b.   inches.
    c.   pixels.
    d.   both A and B
    e.   none of the above

22. Borders and shading are primarily used to:

    a.   make a presentation attractive.
    b.   set apart insignificant text.
    c.   draw attention to important text.
    d.   demonstrate the users creativity.

23. The document orientation in which the height is greater than the width is:

    a.   landscape orientation.
    b.   portrait orientation.
    c.   standard orientation.
    d.   freshman orientation.

24. Often headers and footers contain:

    a.   a page number.
    b.   the name of the document.
    c.   the name of the author.
    d.   the date of printing.
    e.   all of the above

25. _____ are designed to give added information to what is in the main body of text.

    a.   Footnotes
    b.   Footers
    c.   Headers
    d.   Glossaries

26. Print preview is a useful tool for seeing how overall formatting characteristics, such as _____ will affect the appearance of your document.

    a.   margin settings
    b.   headers
    c.   footers
    d.   all of the above

27. Mail merge would be useful to a business that sends the same form letter to many different customers.

    True
    False

28. Web pages are created with a formatting code abbreviated:

    a. HDLP.
    b. HTML.
    c. FTP.
    d. HFTP.

29. Adding graphics and sounds doesn't have much effect on a document's impact.

    True
    False

30. A _____ is a collection of styles that can be applied to a group of similar documents.

    a. style sheet
    b. template
    c. spread sheet
    d. format

31. Style sheets can save time if small changes need to be made to a document.

    True
    False

32. Desktop publishing (DTP) software has had relatively little impact on the publishing and graphic arts industries.

    True
    False

33. The lines between DTP software and word processing software have become more and more defined with time.

    True
    False

34. _____ allows you to make fine adjustments of the spacing between individual letters in a word.

    a. Kerning
    b. Trapping
    c. Tracking
    d. Scrolling

35. _____ allows you to make fine adjustments of the spacing between blocks of text.

    a. Kerning
    b. Trapping
    c. Tracking
    d. Scrolling

36. Desktop publishing software gives you much more control over graphics than does word processing software.

True
False

37. Master pages are preformatted documents that are ready for text to be inserted quickly and easily.

True
False

38. Separate pages created for each color on each page are called:

    a. master pages.
    b. color separations.
    c. Pantone separations.
    d. TruMatch separations.

39. CMYK separation is a method of process color separation.

True
False

40. _____ show precisely where the corners of the page are.

    a. Crop marks
    b. Registration marks
    c. Targets
    d. Trapping marks

41. _____ is the process of adding a tiny overlap to adjacent color elements on a page to account for possible misalignment in the press.

    a. Cropping
    b. Registration
    c. Tracking
    d. Trapping

CHAPTER 8
SPREADSHEETS

Directions

The Textnotes are a note taking and study aid.
- Fill in the Textnote blanks as you proceed through the software instruction.
- Any Textnote reference to computer commands such as "Click..." should be performed by you or your instructor, depending on the instructional setting.

Objectives

When you complete this chapter, you will be able to do the following:

- List the major features of a spreadsheet program.
- Describe some common uses for spreadsheets.
- Explain the structure of a worksheet.
- List several number formats.
- Describe the syntax of a formula.
- Explain the rules of precedence for operators.
- Name the most common types of charts.
- Name several methods for analyzing data.
- Name some future trends for spreadsheets.

A Tool For Working With Numbers

A spreadsheet is a software tool for entering, calculating, manipulating, and analyzing sets of numbers. A spreadsheet is a grid of _____ and _____. An intersection of a column and row is a _____.

The power of a spreadsheet is its ability to manipulate what is in any cell. The cell may contain a number or a _____.

A spreadsheet is like a grid of cells with a programmable _____ attached to each cell. The computer can perform calculations at a blinding speed.

🖐 **NOTE:**   Spreadsheet has come to refer specifically to the software, while worksheet refers to the files that you create with spreadsheet software.

Features of spreadsheet programs:

- A 3-D worksheet is like a pad of worksheets; it lets you calculate from one worksheet to another. In Excel, all worksheets are 3-D, so they are called _____. The individual pages of the workbook are called _____.
- Charts, which are graphic representations of numbers. Charts, also called _____, are created from your data and can use dramatic graphic and 3-D effects.
- Analysis tools.
- Database management tools to organize information and create _____.
- A programming language for automating commands.
- User interfaces to create worksheets for employees or customers.
- Integration with other programs.

Spreadsheets in Business

Businesses track income and expenses, forecast profits or losses, and analyze sales trends.

- Sales departments calculate sales _____.
- Purchasing departments create invoices to keep running totals of their _____.
- Manufacturing departments keep records of maintenance.
- Personnel departments track wages, salaries, and benefits for employees.
- Marketing departments explore the costs of new projects.
- Accounting personnel prepare budgets for financial planning.

Other Professional Uses

- Engineering - used for advanced calculations
- Scientists - applying statistical data

Spreadsheets for Home Users

Use a spreadsheet to prepare a personal budget that tracks your actual expenses and then compares them to your budget.

Creating A Worksheet

Organizing the Data

Your first task is to collect _____ so you can decide how you are going to structure the worksheet.

Designing the Worksheet

Enter a main heading at the top of the worksheet and the text that _____ your rows and columns.

Entering Labels and Values

To enter data, set the position of the cell pointer by clicking the mouse on the cell or by using the arrow keys on the keyboard. The Tab, Home, End, Page Up, and Page Down keys also allow you to move around the worksheet using the keyboard.

Creating Formulas

Know the required _____. The syntax of a formula begins with an equal sign (=) in Excel or a plus sign (+) in Lotus 1-2-3 and Quattro Pro. The + or = is followed by a combination of values, operators, and cell references.

Operators

Operators specify the _____ of operation that you want to perform.

A _____ operator compares the values or labels in two cells. The result of this formula is either True or False. A text operator joins one or more text values into a single combined label.

The Order of Mathematical Operations

When arithmetic operators are used in formulas, spreadsheets calculate the results using the rules of precedence followed in mathematics. The order is as follows:

- Exponentiation
- Negation
- Multiplication and division
- Addition and subtraction

In order to change the order of precedence to suit your needs, you add _____ around any part of the formula that you want to be calculated first.

Cell References

In creating a formula, it is best to use a cell reference rather than to input the cell's data again. The most common method is to refer to the cell by its _____, such as A1, B10, or Y254. If you are referring to a range or block of cells, you can do so by using a colon (:) in Excel and in Lotus 1-2-3 it is done by using two periods (..).

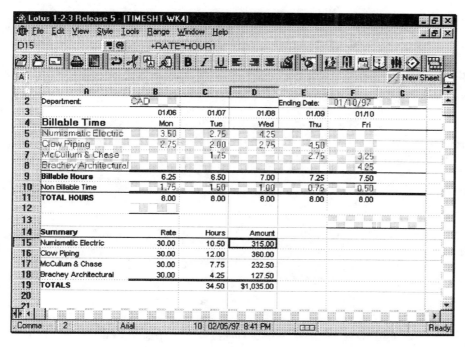

Remember that when you name a cell, that name can be used in a formula as well. When referring to a cell in a different spreadsheet, you must use a special character (the exclamation point (!) in Excel).

Functions

Functions perform specialized calculations automatically. The _____ _____ counts how many values are in a range of cells.

_____ are the values (often cell references) which the function uses in its operation.

The most common is the _____ function that adds a list of numbers to get a total sum.

The leading spreadsheet offers hundreds of functions:

ABS	=	Absolute Value (positive) value of an argument
MAX	=	Maximum value of arguments
PV	=	Present value of an investment
Round	=	Number rounded to a specified number of digits

Editing the Worksheet

Spreadsheet programs make it easy to _____ , _____ , or _____ the contents of cells, and insert or delete rows and columns. Anything you input, you can change. Another feature of spreadsheets is _____ cell references.

Opposite of relative cell references are _____ cell references, which keep the cell references from changing when a cell is moved.

Formatting Values, Labels, and Cells

Numbers can appear as dollars and cents, percentage, dates, times, and fractions. They can be shown with or without commas, decimal points, and so forth.

Dates and times are a special category of numbers. Spreadsheets also offer a choice of fonts and type styles, shadowed borders, and graphics.

Adding Charts

The purpose of a chart is to make the data easier to understand.

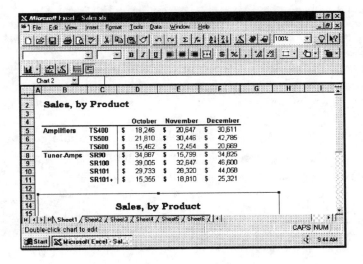

Analyzing the Data

When your worksheet's basic format is complete and you have created any necessary charts, you can use the worksheet to _____ the data. Even adding up totals is a simple form of analysis, but sometimes you want more. This section shows you three useful techniques: what-if analysis, goal seeking, and sorting.

What-If Analysis

B7			=PMT(B4/12,B5*12,-B3)				
	A	B	C	D	E	F	G
1	**Mortgage Payment Examples**						
2				Other Interest Rate Possibilities			
3	Total Mortgage	$ 125,000			$1,212.68		
4	Interest Rate	8.25%		7.50%	$1,158.77		
5	Years Paid	15		7.75%	$1,176.59		
6				8.00%	$1,194.57		
7	Monthly Payment	$1,212.68		8.25%	$1,212.68		
8				8.50%	$1,230.92		
9							

Using a spreadsheet to test how _____ ___ _ affect numeric results is called what-if analysis.

Goal Seeking

Goal seeking finds _____ for one or more cells that make the result of a formula equal to a value you specify.

Sorting

You can sort the data, or select only the records that meet certain criteria, and then perform calculations on the results.

Printing the Worksheet

The ability to create a _____ _____ of your worksheet is vital. Worksheets are not usually the _____ and _____ of the ordinary printer's paper, so it can be divided into paper-sized segments. Other print options include:

- Fit to page
- Scaling

- Landscape printing
- Print preview

Advanced Tools

_____ are a series of recorded commands that automate a task.

_____ collapses the worksheet to show only subtotals and totals, or only totals.

Auditing:

1. Zooming out to see the entire worksheet at one glance.
2. Viewing the formulas in the cells instead of their results.
3. Viewing explanatory notes that have been attached to cells.
4. Automatically going to a cell that is referred to by a cell or that depends on another cell.
5. Creating tracers, which show the relationships between cells graphically.

Norton Workshop: A Worksheet To Analyze Sales

In this Norton Workshop, you will see how Eric Sawitsky, owner of Skywalk Copier Sales, creates a worksheet to analyze sales over the last three years and to project next year's sales. He wants to see the trends over the past three years (1995, 1996, and 1997) and analyze what factors relate most closely to his net profit. He has two theories that he wants to test:

1. The more salespeople he has, the higher his net profit value.
2. The more he spends on advertising, the higher his net profit value.

His data for the worksheet comes from three profit and loss statements, each of which he will place on separate sheets. He names the sheets 1995, 1996, and 1997, and then imports the profit and loss statements to the three sheets.

Eric names a new sheet "Analysis" to consolidate information from the three sheets 1995, 1996, and 1997. He then creates the basic structure.

	A	B	C	D
1	Skywalk Copier Sales			
2				
3		1995	1996	1997
4				
5	Net Profit			
6	Advertising			
7	No. of Sales People			

Now, he is ready to enter data. He clicks on cell B5 of the Analysis sheet, types an equal sign (=) and then clicks on cell B32 in sheet 1995. He presses Enter and the cell reference appears in the Analysis sheet.

Eric enters the six formulas in cells B5 through D6. Now, he types in the number of salespeople for each year to complete the sheet.

Now, Eric is ready to do some analysis. He starts by making a graph. He selects the data and clicks on the Chart button. He decides to use a line graph because it is useful for showing trends over a period of time.

The problem is that the scale of the number of salespeople is so different from the scale of advertising and net profit. He double-clicks on the y-axis and chooses the Logarithmic Scale option in the Format Axis dialog box. A logarithmic scale is useful when the scales are far apart.

Eric feels he needs more specific information about the relationship between net profit, advertising, and the number of salespeople. The first step is to calculate the percentage change in his three variables from year to year. He decides to transpose the rows and columns and copy his data to a new sheet called "Percent Increase." Then he insets the % Increase label after 1996 and 1997.

Now, he is ready to develop the formulas he needs. The formula bar shows the formula for cell B6. Notice the parentheses, which are necessary to make the spreadsheet calculate the subtraction before the division.

B6		=(B5-B4)/B4				
	A	B	C	D	E	F
1	Skywalk Copier Sales					
2						
3		Net Profit	Advertising	No. of Sales People		
4	1995	33,467	14,970	3		
5	1996	36,533	16,367	3		
6	% Increase	9.2%	9.3%	0.0%		
7	1997	38,018	17,114	4		
8	% Increase	4.1%	4.6%	33.3%		
9						

It is now clear that net profit and advertising always increase in similar amounts, whereas the number of salespeople increases in a way that is not connected to net profit. Of course, he knows that he would have to examine the data for more years to be certain that the relationship is causal, but he is satisfied that he has found a clue to his profits.

Back in the Analysis sheet, Eric uses a statistical function, TREND, to see what 1998 might bring. He selects the cells that contain net profits for three years and asks for a fourth number. These are the arguments for the function. The result shows that if the current trend continues, his net profit will be $40,556 in 1998.

This is interesting and helpful information, but Eric is not willing to accept a continuation of the same trend. His goal is a 10 percent increase in net profits. He decides to use Goal Seek to find out the dollar amount of net profit if it increased by 10 percent.

Returning to his "Percent Increase" sheet, Eric adds labels for 1998 and % Increase. He copies the % Increase formula from cell B8 to cell B10 under Net Profit. Then, he uses the Goal Seek command. In the Goal Seek dialog box he completes his request.

Eric duplicates the process for advertising. He figures that if advertising and net profit are so closely related, this will provide him with useful information about how much to spend on advertising next year.

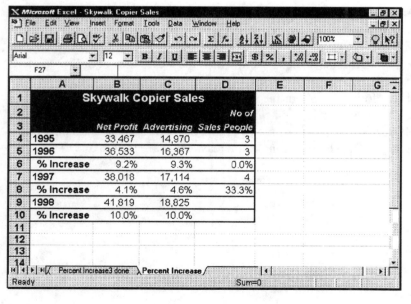

Finally, he is ready to format the tables. He chooses a suitable format from the list of built-in formats, using the preview box to decide which format he wants.

What To Expect In The Future

Trends in spreadsheet programs generally mirror the rest of the software industry. Top spreadsheet programs now come as "_____ _____." This is a package of several programs, including:

- Spreadsheet programs
- Word processors
- Drawing or presentation graphics programs

These office suites make it easy to learn and use programs together.

_____ _____ is another trend. Companies create networks, share information, and then must use it simultaneously. This approach makes it easy for groups to work on a project together.

Finally, creating _____ for frequently performed tasks can reduce data-entry time and alleviate monotonous spreadsheet responsibilities. Excel's *Wizard* and Lotus' *Assistants* do this now.

CHAPTER OUTLINE ACTIVITY

INSTRUCTIONS: The Chapter Outline Activity lists the instructional concepts and topics of this chapter in the order in which they appear. Fill in the outline's blanks with the correct word or phrase to better understand the chapter concepts. The number of blanks represent the number of words per response, while the length of the blanks do not represent the word length.

A Tool For Working With Numbers
Spreadsheets in Business
Other Professional Uses
Spreadsheets for Home Users

Creating A Worksheet

_____ _____ _____

_____ _____ _____

Entering _____ _____ _____
Creating Formulas

_____

_____ _____ _____

_____ _____

Cell _____

_____

Editing the Worksheet

_____ Values, Labels, and Cells
Adding Charts
Analyzing the Data

_____ - ____ _____

Goal _____

_____
Printing the Worksheet

Advanced Tools

Norton Workshop: A Worksheet To Analyze Sales

What To Expect In The Future

REVIEW QUESTIONS

1. The power of the spreadsheet lies in the fact that cells can contain _____ , which calculate numbers based on numbers or formulas in other cells.

    a. packets
    b. figures
    c. formulas
    d. all of the above
    e. none of the above

2. A spreadsheet is like a grid of cells with a programmable _____ attached to each cell.

    a. calculator
    b. timer
    c. dictionary
    d. all of the above
    e. none of the above

3. Businesses will use a spreadsheet for:

    a. keeping track of income and expenses.
    b. forecasting profits or losses.
    c. analyzing sale trends.
    d. all of the above.
    e. none of the above.

4. Engineers and biologists use spreadsheets often to calculate and organize.

    True
    False

5. Many people use a spreadsheet as a simple database manager to keep track of their _____ .

    a. paid bills
    b. books
    c. family's birthdays
    d. all of the above
    e. none of the above

6. Deciding which data is relevant is important when creating a worksheet.

    True
    False

7. A worksheet has many limits to the way it can be designed.

   True
   False

8. A cell pointer identifies the _____ cell.

   a. empty
   b. active
   c. available
   d. all of the above
   e. none of the above

9. In order to create a formula, you must know the _____.

   a. syntax
   b. code
   c. unicode
   d. all of the above
   e. none of the above

10. A text operator compares the values or labels in two cells.

    True
    False

11. The following is the order in which spreadsheets calculate results:

    a. Negation, exponentiation, multiplication and division, and addition and subtraction.
    b. Addition and subtraction, multiplication and division, exponentiation, and negation.
    c. Exponentiation, negation, multiplication and division, and addition and subtraction.
    d. All of the above.
    e. None of the above.

12. When you want to refer to other values in the worksheet, a cell reference can be used to save the time of inputting a cell's data.

    True
    False

13. _____ are the values (often cell references) which the function uses in its operation.

    a. Indexes
    b. Objects
    c. Arguments
    d. All of the above
    e. None of the above

14. When editing a spreadsheet program, you can copy, move, or delete rows, but you are unable to add rows.

    True
    False

15. Numbers can be formatted as _____.

    a. dollars
    b. dates
    c. fractions
    d. all of the above
    e. none of the above

16. The best way to present the data from a spreadsheet to an audience would be with a
    _____.

    a. chart
    b. report
    c. list
    d. all of the above
    e. none of the above

17. _____ analysis can be as simple as replacing a value in a cell that affects other cells, or it can involve the use of data tables, and scenarios or versions.

    a. Goal seeking
    b. What-if
    c. Collective
    d. All of the above
    e. None of the above

18. Spreadsheet programs offer the ability to create, sort, and select from lists of data.

    True
    False

19. You can use a macro to enter data, format worksheets or files, and calculate complex formulas with variable data.

    True
    False

CHAPTER 9
DATABASE MANAGEMENT

Directions

The Textnotes are a note taking and study aid.
- Fill in the Textnote blanks as you proceed through the software instruction.
- Any Textnote reference to computer commands such as "Click..." should be performed by you or your instructor, depending on the instructional setting.

Objectives

When you complete this chapter, you will be able to do the following:

- Distinguish between data and information.
- Define database and database management systems (DBMS) software.
- Describe the features of a DBMS.
- Describe the most common database structures: flat-file, relational, hierarchical, network, and object-oriented.
- Explain the purpose of the most common field types: text, numeric, data and time, logical, counter, memo, and binary.
- Discuss the methods for designing and implementing a DBMS.

Data And Information

Important distinctions that exist between data and information:

- Data consists of the raw _____ or items that are gathered and stored.
- _____ is the product or result of using a DBMS to assemble the data into a meaningful form.

Database management systems are designed to perform several functions:

- Collect relevant data.
- Preserve data for later use.
- Organize data into logical and meaningful sets.
- Create meaningful subsets of data for specific purposes.
- Obtain meaningful subsets for the data in printed form.

The Database-DBMS Relationship

Large companies and organizations rely heavily on _____ or _____ DBMSs to handle immense data resources. DBMSs make it possible to do various routine tasks:

- _____ thousands of records by zip code prior to a bulk mailing.
- Comb the same database for all _____ of those New Yorkers who live in boroughs outside Manhattan.
- Print a list of selected records, such as all real estate listings that closed escrow last month.
- Invoice a customer's new car lease, adjust the dealership's inventory, and _____ the service department's mailing list.

The Database

Data in a database is most commonly viewed in a 2-dimensional table consisting of a _____.

The entire collection of related data in the table is referred to as a _____.

A set of recipe cards provides another way in which you can _____ the relationship between a database file, its records, and its fields.

Flat-File Databases

Flat-file databases can be quite useful for certain single-user or _____ group situations. These databases are limited in that there are no links to, or relationships with, other tables.

The Relational Database Structure

Database structure is a model or design that provides the conceptual _____ for a database.

_____ _____, which is the most prevalent in today's business organizations, represents a database made up of a set of tables which are somehow related. Multiple tables in this kind of database make it possible to handle many data management tasks.

Other Database Structures

- Hierarchical database
- Network database
- Object-oriented database

Data items, along with their associated characteristics, attributes, and procedures are grouped into complex items called _____.

A procedure refers to the processing or handling that can be associated with an object.

The DBMS

DBMSs:

- Make it possible to harness _____ data collections efficiently.
- Allow multiple users to _____ data, _____ it (if necessary), and _____ simple and complex requests to obtain and work with selected records.
- Provide extremely _____ access and retrieval from large databases.

Working With A Database

The _____ is the visual tool you use to perform the important DBMS functions that manage data productively.

Creating Tables

Setting Field Data Types

1. Name the field and briefly indicate what it contains.
2. Specify the field _____.

   - Text or character fields, also called alphanumeric fields
   - Numeric fields
   - Date or time fields
   - Logical fields
   - Binary fields
   - Counter fields
   - Memo fields

3. Specify the field _____.

Field Names

Setting Data-Entry Validation

To ensure data is properly entered in the field, DBMS allows you to set up devices called _____, pictures, or field formats that validate or convert what is typed at the keyboard. Regardless of the name, the device accepts only valid _____ and controls the entry's display format.

Viewing Records

The way data appears on-screen contributes to how well users can work with it.

Filtering Records

Filters are used as one way to limit the information that appears on-screen. They display those records that satisfy the condition, while hiding, or filtering out, those records that do not satisfy the condition.

Using Forms

Forms are used to _____ a record to the user's liking. Most forms in DBMSs are customized by taking objects that represent _____ and placing them in exact locations on a special layout area of the screen.

Sorting Records

One of the most powerful features of DBMSs is their ability to sort a table of data rapidly.

When sorting records, an important consideration is to determine the sort order:

- Ascending sort order
- Descending sort order

How a DBMS Locates Records

Despite how records have been sorted in a table, the DBMS uses a special table called an _____ to locate and access records quickly.

The index stores an association between one field and the physical record number in the original table.

Ensuring Unique Records with a Primary Key

The primary key is a field or set of fields that defines a default record order for the table, ensuring that the table contains no duplicates.

It is often necessary to set _____ conditions for more than one field because users frequently organize records according to the contents of fields other than the _____ _____ field.

Querying a Database

Each of the following is an example of a query:

- Allow the DBMS to locate records.
- Establish relationships or links between tables to update records.
- List a subset of records.

- Perform calculations.
- Delete obsolete records.
- Perform other data management tasks.

SQL: The Language of a Query

The standardized language in many DBMSs is known as SQL. The SQL statement provides a description of data contained in a database so the _____ can locate and use the desired data as defined by the user.

Query by Example

Most SQL or query statements are done behind the scenes, which allows a user to _____ _____ _____ (_____).

With QBE, you specify the search criteria by typing values or _____ into the fields for a QBE form or grid.

Generating Reports

A report is printed information that, like a query result, is assembled by gathering data based on user-supplied criteria.

Reports can range from simple lists of records to _____ formats for special purposes.

Norton Workshop: Applying A DBMS In A Business Environment

In the following workshop, we will explore a practical situation in which a user creates, modifies, and uses a database within a commercial DBMS product.

Kelly owns and operates a home mail-order business to distribute three educational software products that she has developed. She needs to create an efficient system for keeping records of her customers, and for processing and managing orders.

Designing the Database and Creating the Tables

First, Kelly must design the database and create the tables. She does this by jotting down a rough diagram of the tables she will set up as separate database files.

She uses this plan to think about the table names; the number, names, and types of fields that will organize the data each will store; and the relationships among the tables.

Kelly begins by creating the table's _____ in a special table design window.

She names the first field Customer ID and sets it up as the table's primary key, provided by the DBMS. She then enters the field names for the next 12 fields, which are all text fields. Kelly names the table "Customers" and saves the table to a disk. She then customizes the table by changing the field size limits and by creating data entry masks.

She then creates two more database tables that will store her product inventory and purchase orders. She uses _____ view to enter the records for her three multimedia titles directly in the Products table.

Kelly then uses another special window to establish relationships among her tables. She selects all three tables, represented by field list boxes, and then drags the fields that are common to her tables from one field list box to the next to establish the links between them efficiently. The DBMS product Kelly is using displays a "join" line between the field list boxes that represent the _____ tables.

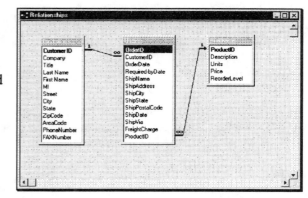

Creating a Data-Entry Form

Next, Kelly must create a _____ _____ for entering her customers' records.

She creates a header, adds drop shadows behind the field boxes, changes fonts, modifies and deletes labels, and adds graphic objects.

Entering and Modifying Data

She then uses her customized form to enter records for her customers. Kelly will use the DBMS's Find command to search for characters. She applies a filter that lists those records based on the criteria she has entered.

When the filter is applied, a Datasheet displays only those records meeting her criteria in the Orders Table Window.

Querying the Database

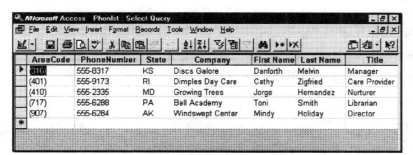

She then uses the query function to generate a list of specific customers to ensure that she calls all the correct customers at the correct time.

We see the list in Datasheet view.

Generating a Summary Report

Kelly uses the DBMS's report generator to display and print a monthly summary that breaks down the current month's sales activity by product.

What To Expect In The Future

Relational databases will be refined to allow users greater flexibility in _____ data, _____ data management procedures, and using existing data resources in a variety of applications.

DBMS interfaces are likely to become more "alive" with _____, animation, and sound. The "learning curve" for users will be reduced significantly as the design and data manipulation process becomes more of a customization task, _____ procedures to the specific needs of organizations.

CHAPTER OUTLINE ACTIVITY

INSTRUCTIONS: The Chapter Outline Activity lists the instructional concepts and topics of this chapter in the order in which they appear. Fill in the outline's blanks with the correct word or phrase to better understand the chapter concepts. The number of blanks represent the number of words per response, while the length of the blanks do not represent the word length.

Data And Information

The _____ - ____ Relationship
The Database
    Flat-File Database
    The Relational Database Structure
    Other Database Structures
The DBMS

Working With A Database
Creating Tables

_____ _____ ____ _____

_____ _____ - _____ _____
Viewing Records

_____ _____

_____ _____
Sorting Records

_____ __ _____ _____ _____

_____ __ _____ ___ __ _____
Querying a Database

____: ___ _____ __ __ _____

_____ ___ _____
Generating Reports

Norton Workshop: Applying A DBMS In A Business Environment
Designing the Database and Creating the

_____

Creating a _____ - _____ form

Entering and Modifying _____

_____ the Database

Generating a _____ Report

What To Expect In The Future

REVIEW QUESTIONS

1. _____ consist(s) of the raw facts or items that are gathered and stored.

   a. Information
   b. Data
   c. Folders
   d. All of the above
   e. None of the above

2. A database that consists of a single data table is a flat-file database.

   True
   False

3. A relational database is the most prevalent in today's business organization.

   True
   False

4. The hierarchical database organizes records by type.

   True
   False

5. A(n) _____ structure groups data items and their associated characteristics, attributes, and procedures into complex items called objects.

   a. relational database
   b. network database
   c. object-oriented database
   d. all of the above
   e. none of the above

6. A database contains a collection of miscellaneous facts.

   True
   False

7. DBMSs allow multiple users to _____.

   a. access data
   b. modify data
   c. construct simple and complex requests to obtain records
   d. all of the above
   e. none of the above

8. Numeric fields store purely numeric data.

   True
   False

9. Counter fields store one of only two possible values.

   True
   False

10. _____ will validate characters and control the entry's display format.

    a. Devices
    b. Masks
    c. Field formats
    d. All of the above
    e. None of the above

11. A _____ is one way to limit information which appears on-screen.

    a. filter
    b. mask
    c. device
    d. all of the above
    e. none of the above

12. A form is a screen that displays data for a single record.

    True
    False

13. _____ are special tables that DBMSs use to locate records quickly in a table.

    a. Masks
    b. Filters
    c. Indexes
    d. All of the above
    e. None of the above

14. Like an index, the primary key not only allows for quick access to particular records, but it also confines the field to unique entries, ensuring there are no duplicates.

    True
    False

15. _____ is an example of organizing records in descending sort order.

    a. A to Z
    b. 0 to 9
    c. 3 to 12
    d. All of the above
    e. None of the above

16. SQL is a special query language for communicating with a database.

    True
    False

17. SQL is an interface for queries that allows the DBMS to collect the facts about a query from the user and to compose the query's QBE statement by itself.

    True
    False

18. A _____ is a user-constructed statement that describes data and sets criteria so the DBMS can gather the relevant data and construct specific information.

    a. mask
    b. filter
    c. query
    d. all of the above
    e. none of the above

19. Report generators in most DBMSs create reports from queries.

    True
    False

CHAPTER 10
THE INTERNET

Directions

The Textnotes are a note taking and study aid.
- Fill in the Textnote blanks as you proceed through the software instruction.
- Any Textnote reference to computer commands such as "Click…" should be performed by you or your instructor, depending on the instructional setting.

Objectives

When you complete this chapter, you will be able to do the following:

- Explain how the Internet got started.
- Understand the structure of Internet addresses.
- Describe the major features of the Internet: e-mail, News, Telnet, FTP, Archie, Gopher, Veronica, and the World Wide Web.
- Describe the ways in which a PC can access the Internet.

Background And History: An Explosion Of Connectivity

In 1969, Advanced Research Projects Agency (ARPA) started a system called ARPANET which planted the seeds for the _____.

NSFnet was a higher-capacity network which was created to compliment ARPANET.

The link between ARPANET, NSFnet, and other networks was called the Internet.

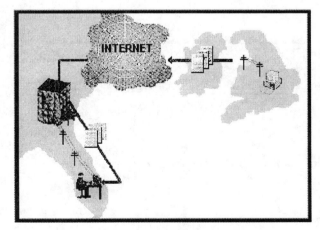

The original ARPANET shut down in 1990, and NSFnet was shut down in 1995, but the _____ still remains.

Today, the Internet connects thousands of _____ and millions of users around the world.

How The Internet Works

The Internet itself is the _____ that carries data between computers.

TCP/IP: The Universal Language of the Internet

Protocols control the timing and data for all computers connected to the Internet. TCP/IP:

- enables _____ which run on different kinds of computers the ability to communicate.
- identifies individual computers and exchanges _____ between computers.

A Network of Networks–Backbones and Gateways

Computers are connected to smaller networks that connect through gateways to the Internet backbone.

Addressing Schemes– IP and DNS Addresses

All computers on the Internet have an _____ by which mail is sent and received.

Internet Protocol (IP) is a four-part numeric address.

Domain Name System (DNS) is a two-part word address.

Big corporations or institutes may have subdomains.

Clients and Servers

A server:

- stores files.
- acts as a gatekeeper for access to data or programs from other computers.

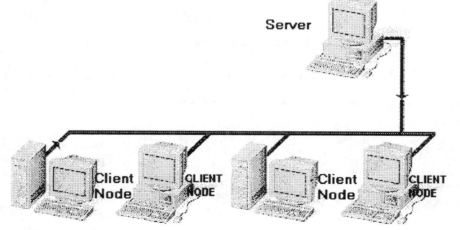

A client application program on a user's computer will go to a server for information.

Major Features Of The Internet

E-Mail

E-Mail is the most common use of the Internet. E-Mail works as a store-and-forward system:

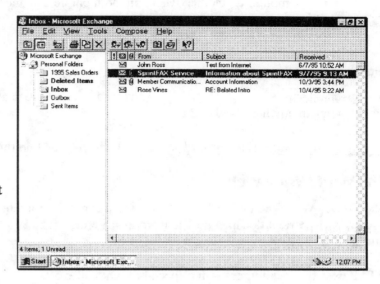

- Sent messages are passed to a post office server.
- The destination address is identified, then passed through the Internet.
- The message is stored at a mail server until the recipient comes looking for it.

_____ is a mailing list that sends the same message to many names.

News

The Internet supports a _____ _____ _____ with more than 10,000 topics called the News. News groups are organized into categories called domains.

_____ is a system in which most widely distributed news groups are apart. Usenet has six "most commonly used" domains with many more "alternative" _____.

A _____

_____ _____

(_____) list is posted once or twice a month for quick reference.

Subscribing to a news group is a three-step process:

STEP #1- Download list of available news groups.
STEP #2- Choose the group that interests you.
STEP #3- Select the article you want to read.

Telnet–Remote Access to Distant Computers

_____ is an Internet tool which obtains information by providing access to a distant host system.

FTP

_____ _____ _____ (_____) is an Internet tool used to copy files from one computer to another. There are both public and anonymous FTP archives.

The _____ is an index used to help locate a file.

Gopher

A Gopher organizes _____ and resources into logical menus. A Gopher menu can include links to anything on the Internet.

_____ is a keyword search tool which helps find things within the Gopher menus.

The World Wide Web

The World Wide Web (WWW) was created to incorporate footnotes, figures, and cross-references into online hypertext documents. The internal structure of the World Wide Web is built on a set of rules called _____ _____ _____ (_____).

HTTP uses Internet addresses in a special format called a _____ _____ _____ (_____). Documents that use HTTP are known as Web pages.

Many Web sites contain a top-level home page that can provide additional pages for more information. _____ is an extensive directory with a menu that lists thousands of Web sites, organized by topic.

Online Services and BBSs

An online service is a company that offers services on a subscription basis. More popular services today include American Online, CompuServe, Microsoft Network, and Prodigy.

_____ _____ (_____) is a free service that is run by individuals. BBSs are normally limited to discussion groups, also known as a bulletin board or news group. A _____ _____ is a live group discussion similar to a conference call.

LEXIS/NEXIS is a well known online service that specializes in two databases instead of just offering general information.

Internet Features in Application Programs

As the Internet has grown, application programs will continue to integrate Internet functions.

Accessing The Internet

Direct Connection

Direct connection is when the Internet programs run on the local computer.

Connection must be made through a serial data communications port using either Serial Line Interface Protocol (SLIP) or _____ _____ _____ _____ (_____).

Remote Terminal Connection

A remote terminal connection to the Internet exchanges commands and data in ASCII text format with a host computer. This kind of Internet access is known as a _____ _____.

Gateway Connection

Networks that use some Internet services are able to use gateways that convert commands and data to and from _____/_____ format.

Most businesses and individuals obtain access through an Internet Service Provider (ISP), which supplies the backbone connection.

Connecting Through a LAN

If the LAN uses TCP/IP protocols for communication within the network, simply connect the Internet through a _____.

If the LAN uses a different kind of local protocol, a bridge converts it from TCP/IP. When a LAN has an Internet connection, that connection extends to every computer on the LAN.

Connecting Through a Modem

If there is no LAN on site, an isolated computer can connect to a network through a serial data communications port and a _____.

High-Speed Data Links

High-speed data circuits are available to speed up an Internet connection.

_____ _____ _____ _____ (__v__) is a digital telephone service that commands voice, data, and control signaling through a single circuit.

Other Online Services

America Online, Microsoft Network, and CompuServe provide services which are preferred by many, regardless of their slightly higher rates.

Connecting A PC To The Internet

Integrated Internet Software Packages

Software packages have several advantages:

- A common interface design will result in easier _____.
- There will be a single contact for technical support and product upgrades.
- There is little chance of any _____ between the software and the network.

Norton Workshop: Research Using The Web

In this section, we will go through a step-by-step process on using the World Wide Web to find out information about England and France for an upcoming vacation.

- Through the Yahoo! search engine, we find the URL for the Electronic Telegraph, an online version of a London newspaper.
- Log onto the account with a local ISP.
- Open the Web browser.
- Enter the URL for the Electronic Telegraph.
- The _____ downloads the home page of the online publication, direct from London.

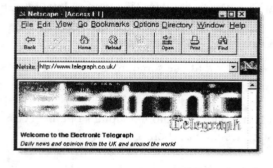

- Register as a visitor by typing in "guest" for account name and password name.
- Several choices are available.
- Click on the Features icon to see the feature stories.
- There is an article on touring Paris, so take the first link to a Paris _____ _____.
- Accessing the scroll bar, we see more specific information about Paris.
- The Web browser program will take us back to the Paris home page, where we find links to "Museums."

- Going back to the home page will offer more areas to explore.
- It is possible to print everything, or just select findings.
- Log off.

We have just gone through what is known as "_____ _____," or exploring the vast stores of information on the World Wide Web.

What To Expect In The Future

The Internet will expand and change in several ways:

- Faster _____.
- More _____.
- New _____ and "virtual reality" services.
- Distributed _____-_____ applications

It is highly probable that the Internet will be used universally, as the radio and television are today.

CHAPTER OUTLINE ACTIVITY

INSTRUCTIONS: The Chapter Outline Activity lists the instructional concepts and topics of this chapter in the order in which they appear. Fill in the outline's blanks with the correct word or phrase to better understand the chapter concepts. The number of blanks represent the number of words per response, while the length of the blanks do not represent the word length.

Background And History: An Explosion Of Connectivity

How The Internet Works
TCP/IP: The Universal Language of the Internet

A Network of Networks–Backbones and

_____

Addressing Schemes–_____ and DNS Addresses

Clients and Servers

Major Features Of The Internet

_____-_____

News

Telnet–_____ _____ ____

_____ _____

_____

_____
The World Wide Web

Online _____ _____ _____

_____ Features in Application Programs

Accessing The Internet

_____ Connection

_____ _____ Connection

_____ Connection

Connecting Through a _____

Connecting Through a _____

_____ - _____ _____ _____

Other Online Services

Connecting A PC To The Internet
Integrated Internet Software Packages

Norton Workshop: Research Using The Web

What To Expect In The Future

REVIEW QUESTIONS

1. _____ planted the seeds for the Internet.

   a. ARPANET
   b. NETPLAN
   c. Telnet
   d. all of the above
   e. none of the above

2. The network _____ is the central structure that connects other elements of the network.

   a. gateway
   b. center
   c. backbone
   d. all of the above
   e. none of the above

3. The Internet works because every computer connected to it uses the same set of rules and procedures known as domains.

   True
   False

4. TCP/IP software looks different on different kinds of computers, but it always presents the same appearance to the network.

   True
   False

5. _____ is an example of a subdomain address.

   a. Washington.edu
   b. Genetics.washington.edu
   c. Evolution.genetics.washington.edu
   d. All of the above
   e. None of the above

6. A(n) _____ application program on a user's computer requests information through the network from a server.

   a. IP
   b. client
   c. domain
   d. all of the above
   e. none of the above

7. A _____ server stores an e-mail message in a mailbox until the recipient comes looking for it.

   a. post office
   b. box
   c. mail
   d. all of the above
   e. none of the above

8. Many of the most widely distributed news groups are part of a system called _____.

   a. Usenet
   b. Inet
   c. National
   d. all of the above
   e. none of the above

9. _____ are major categories in which news groups are organized.

   a. Selections
   b. Domains
   c. Topics
   d. All of the above
   e. None of the above

10. Telnet is the Internet tool used to copy files from one computer to another.

    True
    False

11. _____ exist in FTP archives.

    a. Weather maps
    b. Recipes
    c. Programs for Windows, Macintosh, UNIX, and other operating systems
    d. All of the above
    e. None of the above

12. _____ is a keyword search tool that finds and displays items from Gopher menus.

    a. Yahoo!
    b. Lookout
    c. Veronica
    d. All of the above
    e. None of the above

13. _____ organizes widely scattered resources into a seamless whole.

    a. Veronica
    b. The Web
    c. Yahoo!
    d. All of the above
    e. None of the above

14. Yahoo! is an extensive directory with a menu that lists thousands of Web sites, organized by topic, and a search engine that looks for specific words in titles.

    True
    False

15. _____ is a popular online service.

    a. America Online
    b. CompuServe
    c. Microsoft Network
    d. All of the above
    e. None of the above

16. A discussion group is also called a chat line.

    True
    False

17. The Internet has become a part of daily life for many computer users as many application programs have integrated Internet functions.

    True
    False

18. Serial Line Interface Protocol and Point-to-Point Protocol are two methods for creating a direct connection through a _____.

    a. post office server
    b. phone line
    c. mail server
    d. all of the above
    e. none of the above

19. TCP/IP application programs and protocols all run on the host.

    True
    False

20. Most local networks connect directly to the Internet backbone because it is inexpensive.

    True
    False

21. A _____ is another computer that stores and forwards sets of data to other computers on the Internet.

    a. bridge
    b. packet
    c. port
    d. all of the above
    e. none of the above

22. A computer can connect to a network through a serial data communications port and a modem using:

    a. a shell account.
    b. a terminal emulation program.
    c. direct TCP/IP connection with a SLIP or PPP account.
    d. all of the above.
    e. none of the above.

23. Fiber optics, microwave, and other technologies can establish an Internet connection that is much faster than a modem link.

    True
    False

24. Online services provide their own conferences, news reports, live chat groups, magazines, and newspapers.

    True
    False

25. In most cases, the applications in a suite have different interface designs, so they are not easily understood or used.

    True
    False

CHAPTER 11
GRAPHICS

Directions

The Textnotes are a note taking and study aid.
- Fill in the Textnote blanks as you proceed through the software instruction.
- Any Textnote reference to computer commands such as "Click…" should be performed by you or your instructor, depending on the instructional setting.

Objectives

When you complete this chapter, you will be able to do the following:

- Explain the purpose and use of graphics software.
- Differentiate between paint and draw programs.
- Discuss the differences between the major categories of graphics software.
- List the most common file formats for bitmap and vector graphics.
- Explain the appropriate uses of different graphics software packages.

Working With Images

Platforms

In the early 1980s, the Apple Macintosh computer and MacPaint software began the era of "art" on the _____ _____.

With the release of powerful graphics software and the beginning of the Postscript printing language, Macintosh became the tool choice for computer artists.

Microsoft's Windows soon brought these capabilities to IBM PCs and _____.

Workstations are reserved for the most demanding graphics projects. Features of the workstation:

- Powerful and fast CPUs
- Large-capacity hard disks
- High-resolution displays
- Lots of RAM

Two of the more popular _____ are the Sun SparcStation and the Silicon Graphics Indigo2.

Types of Graphics Files

Bitmaps Versus Vectors

Graphics programs that work with bitmaps are called paint programs. Bitmap-based graphics software requires you to manipulate the pixels to create _____. Graphics programs that work with vectors are called draw programs. Vector-based graphics software requires you to use _____ to represent lines, shapes, and patterns.

Standard File Formats

In order to share files or move files, one must be familiar with standard file formats. _____ _____ (_____) is the most common format for vector graphics.

Getting Existing Images into Your Computer

Scanners and Cameras

A scanner will _____ and _____ an image directly into the computer, resulting in a bitmap file. A digital camera will store digitized images in memory for transfer into a computer, resulting in a _____ file.

Electronic Photographs

Today, most graphic artists will digitize a photo using a _____. Special processing labs will scan images and save the resulting file in a format called PhotoCD (PCD).

Clip Art

Clip art is professionally created drawings and graphics available for the _____. _____ _____ is available on CD-ROM, diskettes, or via commercial online services, which can be cut out and glued to a paper layout.

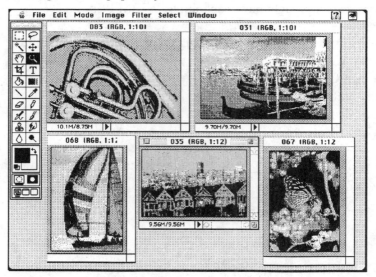

Copyright Issues

Most images that you see in print or on-screen are _____ by the creator or publisher of the image. In order to use an image not created solely on your own, you must contact the _____ _____ for permission.

Graphics Software

Paint Programs

Paint programs keep track of each and every _____ placed on a screen. Paintbrush, chalk, pen, watercolors, airbrush, crayon, and eraser are some of the paint program _____.

This program allows you to make minor adjustments to the image by _____ each pixel until it is exactly as you like it.

A disadvantage to this program is that you are not able to change the entire image as a whole.

Paint programs have unusual _____ _____, such as the ability to convert a scanned photograph into a pencil sketch or to make it look like a Van Gogh oil painting.

Photo-Manipulation Programs

Photo-manipulation programs now take the place of a photographer's darkroom. Images are _____ at pixel level so photo-manipulation programs can control precisely how a picture will look. Photo-manipulation allows one to edit a photograph in various ways:

- Sharpen the _____.
- Adjust the _____.
- Change the colors.
- Remove a dust spot or a scratch on the film.

Draw Programs

Draw programs work by defining every line as a mathematical equation, or _____. Advantages to this program:

- When objects are created, they remain objects to the _____, and therefore they are able to be colored, moved, and copied.
- Images are able to be resized to match the dimension of the paper they will be printed on without any loss in the _____.

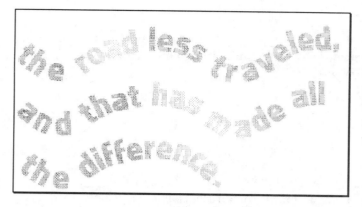

Today, attributes of both the paint program and the draw program have been incorporated into one another, allowing for _____ graphic work.

Computer-Aided Drafting Programs

Computer-Aided Drafting (CAD) takes the place of designing formerly done with a pencil and a ruler on a drafting table. Features of this program:

- High degree of precision
- Ability to define layers
- Capability to add dimensions

- Variety of ways to display or print 3-D objects
- Ability to render an object
- Ability to create a database from a drawing

CAD is such an essential part of the manufacturing process that it is often the first step in _____ - _____ _____ (_____).

3-D Modeling Programs

3-D modeling software enables users to create electronic models of 3-dimensional objects without using CAD software. Types of 3-D modeling programs include:

- Surface modelers build objects by stretching a surface (like a skin) over an underlying wire-frame structure.
- Solids modelers do the same as surface modelers, but they also understand _____ and _____.

- Polygonal modelers combine many tiny polygons to build objects.
- Spline-based modelers build objects using _____ _____ _____, which are rotated on an axis to form a 3-D shape.

Norton Workshop: Creating An Infographic

The following is a step-by-step process of the creation of a newspaper informational graphic, also called infographics, that explains how a train derailment occurred.

1. Photographs are taken of a railroad track to study how train tracks are put together.
2. For more accurate information, a picture from a reference book is scanned and saved, which explains how railroad tracks are put together.
3. The Bezier tool is used to connect lines that can be manipulated into any shape traced over the scanned-in drawing of the railroad track.
4. Editing is done to create a realistic picture.
5. Photo-manipulation is used on an actual photograph of the accident to help readers visualize the scene.
6. The file is saved and imported back into the draw program document.
7. In the draw program, the knife tool is used to "cut" a piece of the railroad track from the drawing to show the break created by the saboteurs who caused the great crash.
8. The Bezier tool is used to show how the track was moved.
9. Descriptive text is added to the drawing to help in the explanation.
10. The graphic is completed and transferred as a computer data file to the newspaper's network.

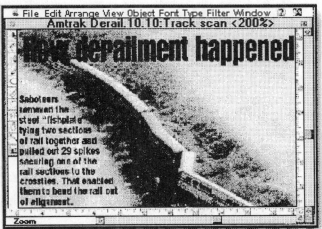

What To Expect In The Future

We will see more advanced _____ software packages which will be more accessible to the public. The continued growth of multimedia has, and will, create an interest in the _____ capabilities of graphic software.

CHAPTER OUTLINE ACTIVITY

INSTRUCTIONS: The Chapter Outline Activity lists the instructional concepts and topics of this chapter in the order in which they appear. Fill in the outline's blanks with the correct word or phrase to better understand the chapter concepts. The number of blanks represent the number of words per response, while the length of the blanks do not represent the word length.

Working With Images
Platforms
Types of Graphics Files

_____ _____ _____

_____ _____ _____
Getting Existing Images into Your Computer

_____ and Cameras
Electronic Photographs

_____ ____

_____ Issues

Graphics Software

_____ Programs

_____-Manipulation Programs

_____ Programs

_____-_____ Drafting Programs

___-___ Modeling Programs

Norton Workshop: Creating An Infographic

What To Expect In The Future

REVIEW QUESTIONS

1. The Apple Macintosh computer along with MacPaint program began the era of "computer art."

   True
   False

2. Workstations are specialized single-user computers which possess _____.

   a. powerful and fast CPUs
   b. large-capacity hard disks
   c. high-resolution displays
   d. all of the above
   e. none of the above

3. Bitmaps are graphic files which are composed of mathematical equations which describe the positions of lines.

   True
   False

4. _____ software is used to edit pixel-by-pixel.

   a. Vector-based
   b. Pixel-based
   c. Bitmap-based
   d. All of the above
   e. None of the above

5. A _____ is a tool which can capture a picture and transfer it directly into the computer.

   a. scanner
   b. copy machine
   c. television
   d. all of the above
   e. none of the above

6. Today, graphic artists use traditional photos translated into digital formats more often than they use photos from digital cameras.

   True
   False

7. Clip art is easily available from many vendors.

    True
    False

8. To avoid any legal issues when copying an image, it is best to contact the copyright holder to receive permission.

    True
    False

9. A paint program:

    a. takes the place of a photographer's darkroom.
    b. works by defining every line as a vector.
    c. keeps track of every pixel placed on a screen.
    d. all of the above.
    e. none of the above.

10. Paint programs are great for handling text.

    True
    False

11. Photo-manipulation is used to manipulate images which are scanned.

    True
    False

12. Once an object in a draw program is created, it remains an object to the computer.

    True
    False

13. A draw program:

    a. takes the place of a photographer's darkroom.
    b. works by defining every line as a vector.
    c. keeps track of every pixel placed on a screen.
    d. all of the above.
    e. none of the above.

14. A Computer-Aided Drafting program:

    a. has the ability to define layers.
    b. takes the place of drafting done with a pencil and ruler on a drafting table.
    c. can add dimensions to a program.
    d. all of the above.
    e. none of the above.

15. Surface modelers build objects using mathematically defined curves, which are rotated on an axis to form a 3-D shape.

    True
    False

16. Polygonal modelers build objects by stretching a surface, like a skin, over an underlying wire-frame structure.

    True
    False

CHAPTER 12
THE NEW MEDIA

Directions

The Textnotes are a note taking and study aid.
- Fill in the Textnote blanks as you proceed through the software instruction.
- Any Textnote reference to computer commands such as "Click…" should be performed by you or your instructor, depending on the instructional setting.

Objectives

When you complete this chapter, you will be able to do the following:

- Explain the concept of interactive multimedia and its role in new communications technologies.
- Describe the ways consumers receive multimedia content.
- Provide examples of multimedia applications for schools, businesses, and the home.
- Describe hypermedia and its role in multimedia presentations.
- Envision how you might use virtual reality.
- Explain the process of creating a multimedia presentation.
- Discuss the impact of digital convergence on the media being produced for mass consumption.

The Power Of Interactivity

The power and low cost of today's PCs have changed the ways in which businesses and individuals _____ and _____ information.

_____, _____, _____, _____, and _____ can all be stored and edited by computers in order to communicate ideas.

Individually, these channels, or _____, of communication are called media.

Any of these media can be combined to produce engaging, multimedia presentations for any audience.

Perhaps one of the most obvious examples of multimedia presentation is _____, where _____ and _____ are combined.

Television adds a dimension to the communication of ideas that sound or pictures alone do not possess.

Interacting with Television

The criticism leveled at television is that information flows in _____ _____, from the TV to the viewer, and does not actively involve a person in the learning process.

Today, the prevalence of inexpensive _____ offers a way to change our passive response to electronic media.

Computers make it possible to create interactive media, in which people can _____ _____ - and even _____ - what they see and hear.

This establishes two-way communication, also known as a _____ _____, making the user an active participant in the communication process.

A good example of this _____ loop is a video game in which information displayed on a TV screen is constantly changing in response to the information coming from the user.

Traditional _____ companies are currently considering ways of changing their now passive programming to more interactive communication.

But, the problem of how to accommodate the interactive communication with broadcast capability is still a _____ hurdle to be solved.

Interacting with Computers

While consumers wait for the deployment of interactive television networks, many other _____-_____ vehicles are already in place:

- CD-ROM - a self-contained interactive program.
- Internet and online services - designed for high-volume, two-way information transfer.

Interactivity also includes interaction between _____ people, not just interaction with a world of faceless computers.

Through _____ _____ or the Internet, millions of people interact with others each day via electronic mail or "live" conversations typed on the keyboard.

Interactivity and Education

_____ computers are an integral part of many classrooms and bring a new level of _____ to learning. Interactive learning helps:

- _____ students to become active participants.
- Students _____ critical thinking and problem-solving skills.
- Build social skills.
- Allow students with a wide range of learning skills to be _____.
- _____ collaboration on projects even across thousands of miles.

At the Workplace

The role of multimedia in the workplace is fast becoming an integral part of many aspects of a company's _____ activities.

Companies are always training employees, especially in the area of the latest _____ _____.

Interactive training courses, called _____ - _____ _____ (_____), are becoming increasingly popular.

These courses can include training on:

- Company policies
- Customized computer systems
- Customer relations

_____ and _____ are taking on new meaning in the age of multimedia.

Interactive electronic catalogs may now be created and distributed either in _____-_____ _____ or presented on a company's _____ _____ _____ _____.

Orders for merchandise can even be placed via the Internet.

_____ is the primary focus of multimedia in business, both _____ and _____ the company. Video conferencing has become a reality for any PC.

Small, affordable _____ and _____ allow two or more people to see and speak with each other by means of their screens.

Documents can also be _____ and _____ simultaneously.

At Home

The goal of _____ _____ is to get the audience to participate.

By far the most popular multimedia products are in the _____ _____.

Video games sold on _____ and _____-_____ for dedicated game machines or for desktop computers are very popular.

Next in popularity may be applications for managing _____ that can assist in such things as:

- Financial planning
- Making investment decisions
- Planning for retirement

Another emerging technology for home use is called _____ _____.

Through a specially made _____ connected to your television, you would be able to select from vast libraries of movies stored in computers at your cable company office.

Instead of making a trip to the video store or waiting for a movie to start on cable, you would be able to order and watch a movie with ease whenever you want.

The New Media

Traditional media companies - _____ _____, _____ _____, and _____ - have begun to look for ways to repackage their existing materials in a multimedia format.

Because of the trend towards computer-based presentations, it is not uncommon to hear multimedia referred to as new media.

More and more, different types of media are being converted to digital form.

As this trend continues, more and more information will begin to travel to the consumer along the same paths - perhaps via _____-_____ or _____ _____ _____.

This streamlining of the information highway is called digital convergence.

Multimedia: Beyond Words

_____ _____ quickly discovered that consumers did not respond well to the simple conversion of the printed page to the computer screen.

The challenge, then, was to make the electronic version of the content more _____, utilizing the special powers that computers have to offer.

Adding Sound, Graphics, Animation, and Video

Adding time-based content, such as

_____,

_____

_____,

and _____,
makes printed text more inviting.

It is important, however, that added media not merely mimic the

_____

_____ and

_____

_____.

It is essential that the _____ of a multimedia program not be overshadowed by

_____.

_____ _____ has only limited appeal and should never outweigh _____.

Platform Considerations for Multimedia

Multimedia publishers must always consider the user's equipment, or _____.

Essential components for a multimedia PC include:

- A fast CPU chip
- Plenty of RAM
- A sound card
- Speakers
- A CD-ROM player

Because technology progresses so rapidly, _____ _____ have become necessary to help multimedia developers predict how much multimedia power should be in users' computers.

In 1995, the Multimedia Personal Computer (MPC) standard, called _____ _____ ____, was introduced. Perhaps the most important issue considered by multimedia developers is that of _____ _____.

The problem here is that high-quality video requires that _____ of bits be transmitted to the monitor every second. Consider this equation:

$$
\begin{array}{rl}
24 & \text{number of bits per pixel} \\
\times\ 480 & \text{number of pixels vertically} \\
\times\ 640 & \text{number of pixels horizontally} \\
\times\ \underline{\ 15\ } & \text{number of frames per second} \\
= 110{,}592{,}000 & \text{bits per second}
\end{array}
$$

Regardless of the video's source, _____ _____ or _____, the wires connecting the source to the monitor or television usually are not capable of transmitting the digital information fast enough.

The capacity for data transmission is known as bandwidth.

One possible solution to the common problem of a _____ in the bandwidth somewhere in the computer system is data compression.

Data compression typically uses _____ _____ of digital source material to strip away unnecessary bits of data prior to sending it across the wire.

At the receiving end, the missing bits are quickly reinserted to produce a copy that is extremely close to the original in quality and detail.

The most common standardized multimedia compression schemes are:

- JPEG (pronounced "jay-peg") - Joint Photographic Experts Group
- MPEG (pronounced "em-peg") - Motion Picture Experts Group
- MPEG-2

Each scheme is sponsored by an industry consortium whose goal is to achieve _____ _____ ____ _____ and _____ - _____ _____ ____ _____.

Hypermedia: User-Directed Navigation

Multimedia programs offer large amounts of information to the user; therefore, being able to find your way through the data is of the utmost importance if the program is to be of value.

Moving about in an electronic information environment is commonly called _____.

Navigation can be as simple as moving to the next page of text like turning the page of a book, but it can also be highly _____, able to jump to locations outside of the normal, linear sequence.

A new term has emerged to describe a _____ _____ where the user can click on one type of media to navigate to the same or other type of media.

This term is hypermedia, a more modern version of a concept called _____.

Both terms refer to a system of navigation where the user can click on a _____, _____, or _____ and be linked to other related items.

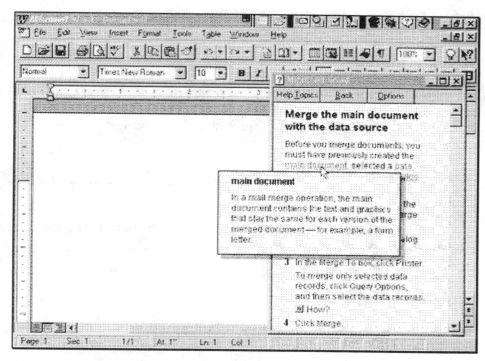

The Help system in Microsoft Word contains many hypertext links.

Clicking on a _____, _____ _____ displays the definition of that word.

Many pages on the _____ _____ _____ contain hypertext links that allow you to navigate to other sections within the Web site or to another site altogether.

Presentation Software: Reaching Your Audience

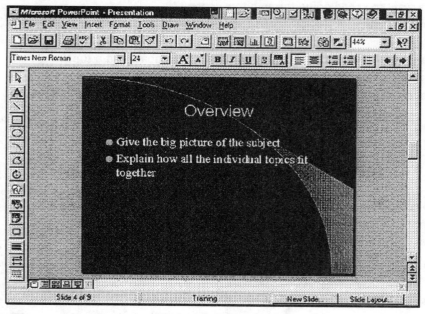

Multimedia computers have changed the way that public _____ are given.

Programs have emerged that make it a simple process to combine static material like text with visual effects like:

- Colorful backgrounds
- Bulleted items
- Animation, video, and sound

These applications are called presentation software.

Virtual Reality: Adding the Third Dimension

It could be said that the most effective computer navigation is when you have the feeling of traveling through a _____-_____ _____.

The recreation on a computer display of what appears to be physical space is called virtual reality.

Devices with _____ _____ process the user's navigational movements and projects the action into virtual space.

Virtual screen scenes can be constructed from _____ _____ _____ or _____.

_____ _____ _____ (_____) is an authoring language used to create 3-D environments on the World Wide Web.

Creating Multimedia

Because of the different types of media and the flexibility in navigation, creating _____ multimedia is difficult.

Defining Your Audience

Imagine yourself, the _____ _____, as someone using or viewing your program, and ask yourself the following questions:

- How much should users know about the subject before the presentation or program begins?
- What do users expect to gain from their experience with the program? Is the goal to learn something? To be entertained?
- How much time will users want to spend going through this content?
- Will users get more out of this content if it is predominantly text, graphics, sound, animation, or video?
- What kind of interaction will users want with the program? Is their feedback via a touch screen, a keyboard and a mouse, or a game controller?
- Will the content or presentation be engaging enough to make users want to linger and to come back again?

Multimedia Design

Planning the overall _____ is often the longest part of the development process.

A common way to start a project is by composing an _____, or _____, of the material to be covered in the development.

Here you would determine the answers to several questions:

- How much information - text, graphics, clickable objects - will appear on each screen?
- How will the user navigate throughout the environment?
- Will the navigation be primarily linear in format, or will the user be able to jump around the entire program?

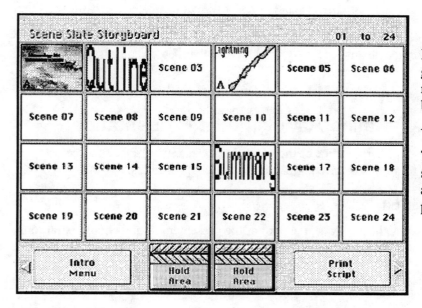

If a program contains a great deal of animation or many different screens, the best design aid is a

_____.

The storyboard consists of sketches of the _____ and _____ in a production.

Choosing the Tools

Many different tools can be used in the development process:

- Word processors
- Graphics software
- Video-capture programs
- Sound editors

When the content is ready, it needs to be assembled in a process called multimedia authoring.

This process requires still another type of software which can:

- understand all the different types of media.
- combine the different types of media.
- control the sequences in which they appear.
- create navigational tools and an interface for the user.

The best approach to the authoring process is to imagine the _____ _____ in the design stage, then locate the _____ that let you come as close to that ideal as possible.

Multimedia Authoring

Multimedia authoring generally is performed by a _____, and is more successful if the programmer has access _____ _____ _____ and a _____ _____ at the outset.

Testing

Software testing must be done by the kinds of people who will be using the programs.

By testing, the programmer can locate any _____ and repair them before unleashing the finished product on the world.

Norton Workshop: Creating A Multimedia Presentation

Carol Keihani, the director of the Boston office of the Maru-Maru Chamber of Commerce, is invited to make presentations to groups of meeting planners at a local conference.

Designing the Presentation

Carol and a writer meet to discuss the audience, the goal of the presentation, and choose what tools to use.

Entering and Formatting the Text

Because this is not a long presentation, the writer, Bryan, starts drafting the text for the _____ in an outliner function.

Bryan can switch the view to the actual slide to see how the text he entered in the outline looks.

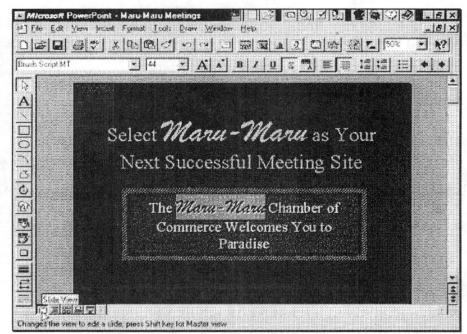

Adding Graphics

Rosa, the graphics designer, looks through the _____ _____ provided with the presentation software for fitting background art, test colors, and bullet characters. The selected template is applied to the presentation. Before Rosa goes to work on some of the animation effects they have planned for other slides, she selects a transitional visual effect between each slide.

Bryan copies a map from an electronic atlas to help the audience understand where Maru-Maru is in relationship to Hawaii. He then pastes the map from the _____ into the slide.

Rosa uses the drawing tools in the presentation package to create an arrow leading from Hawaii to Maru-Maru. The arrow is pasted on the slide. To animate the arrow, Rosa makes selections in the _____ _____ dialog box for the arrow object.

Text providing the current communications facilities available to conference participants is imported from a word processing document.

Rosa adds a video segment showing one of the beaches at sunset. Clicking on the image of the beach plays the movie.

A link is added to allow Carol to navigate to previous sections of the presentation.

Finally, an audio file of traditional island music is added. Clicking on the speaker icon plays the file.

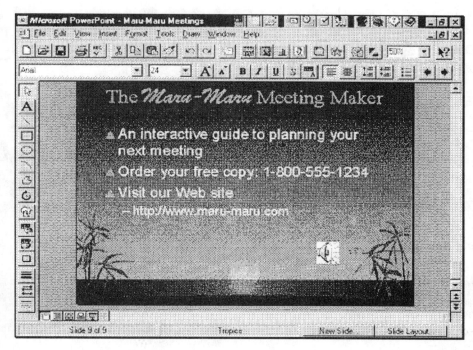

Presenting the Finished Product

Before giving the talk in front of the real audience, Carol must test the presentation program in rehearsals.

_____, _____, and _____ all pay off for Carol, who generates many leads from her presentation the first time she shows it.

What To Expect In The Future

New media will not be new forever as _____ software will certainly increase in the near future.

Great strides in the realm of realistic _____ _____ will occur in the next several years.

The most rapid advances will occur, however, in the delivery of content containing multiple media and interaction.

The exchange of information and ideas will expand and quicken as users get more up-to-the-minute information and share it with people globally via the _____.

CHAPTER OUTLINE ACTIVITY

INSTRUCTIONS: The Chapter Outline Activity lists the instructional concepts and topics of this chapter in the order in which they appear. Fill in the outline's blanks with the correct word or phrase to better understand the chapter concepts. The number of blanks represent the number of words per response, while the length of the blanks do not represent the word length.

The Power Of Interactivity

Interacting with _____

Interacting with _____

Interactivity and _____
At the Workplace
At Home

The New Media
Multimedia: Beyond Words

    Adding _____, Graphics, Animation,

     and _____
    Platform Considerations for Multimedia
Hypermedia: User-Directed Navigation
Presentation Software: Reaching Your
   Audience

    _____ _____: Adding the Third
   Dimension

Creating Multimedia

Defining Your _____

_____ _____
Choosing the Tools
Multimedia Authoring
Testing

Norton Workshop: Creating A Multimedia Presentation

Designing the _____

Entering and _____ the Text

Adding _____
Presenting the Finished Product

What To Expect In The Future

REVIEW QUESTIONS

1. Multimedia refers to:

   a. text.
   b. graphics.
   c. sound.
   d. video.
   e. all of these.

2. _____ allows you to respond to and even control what the viewer sees and hears.

   a. Media
   b. Multimedia
   c. Interactive media
   d. Passive media

3. In the future, television will likely become less passive and more interactive.

   True
   False

4. Interactivity includes interaction between both people and computers.

   True
   False

5. Interactive learning helps in all the following except:

   a. Motivate students to become passive participants.
   b. Students integrate critical thinking and problem-solving skills.
   c. Students build social skills.
   d. Allow students with a wide range of learning skills to be successful.

6. Multimedia applications have had an impact on the corporate but not the consumer side of business.

   True
   False

7. The most popular multimedia products are in the:

   a. financial planning field.
   b. self-help field.
   c. entertainment field.
   d. home-improvement field.

8. Traditional media companies have been relatively unaffected by new media.

   True
   False

9. Both content and creativity are essential elements of effective multimedia.

   True
   False

10. Industry standards, like the Multimedia Personal Computer (MPC) standard, have helped to tailor software production to fit consumers' needs.

    True
    False

11. Perhaps the most important issue considered by multimedia developers is that of:

    a. content.
    b. creativity.
    c. cost.
    d. data compression.

12. A high bandwidth will always prevent a bottleneck during data transmission.

    True
    False

13. The ease of navigation through an electronic environment can increase an application's overall usefulness.

    True
    False

14. Virtual reality could be a useful tool in allowing users to interact in environments that would be difficult or impossible to explore otherwise.

    True
    False

15. Which of the following is not a question to consider during multimedia development?

    a. What is the information being presented?
    b. How will users navigate through the content?
    c. Who will be using the program?
    d. How much will the program cost to produce?
    e. None of these

16. Working from a good script or storyboard can save the developer a lot of time.

    True
    False

17. It is usually best to base your development on the tools you have available.

    True
    False

18. It would be wise to have an experienced programmer test a program designed for beginning users because they could best find any flaws that might exist.

    True
    False